GAMING: THE FUTURE'S LANGUAGE

by

Richard D. Duke

SAGE Publications

Halsted Press Division
JOHN WILEY & SONS
New York—London—Sydney—Toronto

Distributed by Halsted Press, a Division of John Wiley & Sons, Inc., New York

Printed in the United States of America

Library of Congress Cataloging in Publication Data

Duke, Richard D
Gaming: the future's language

1. Game theory. 2. Simulation methods. I. Title.
QA269.D84 519.3 74-14522
ISBN 0-470-22405-3

FIRST PRINTING

To

Stewart D. Marquis

No more dedicated or enlightened teacher has ever crossed my path

TABLE OF CONTENTS

Appendices

LIST OF FIGURES

ACKNOWLEDGEMENTS

This document has emerged over the course of a decade; as a consequence, many people have influenced its development. The search for comprehension of the nature of gaming has brought me into contact with professionals from a wide variety of fields, both at home and abroad. Attendance at hundreds of gaming events, under a wide set of circumstances, has given me exposure to a broad array of audience types. These experiences, cumulatively, have provided the grist from which the notion of the game as a "language" is tentatively advanced.

Acknowledgement is due to Richard L. Meier who was the first to encourage me to explore the phenomenon of gaming. In addition to providing counsel for the development of *Metropolis* and METRO-*APEX*, he also gave considerable support to my various research efforts in gaming during the 1960s.

To acknowledge all who have contributed to this manuscript is impossible; however, special thanks are due to Peter Sandman whose thoughtful criticism has induced a more coherent specification of the concept of the game-specific language. Cathy Greenblat has served as a foil for many of the ideas presented and has been particularly helpful in the process of defining the many variables incident to an intelligent description of gaming. In addition, she was instrumental in the clarification of the Chapter on "Interpretive Criteria."

A special debt is owed to Nancy Stieber, whose quiet, steady competence was invaluable in the preparation of this document. She has worked closely with me from its inception, both by helping in the organization of ideas as well as by challenging the validity of the concepts being developed. In addition to serving as critic artist and editor, she has done the yeoman's tasks inevitably associated with such work.

Financial support for the preparation of this document was provided by the General Electric Foundation. Funding by the Ford Foundation for research and developmental work during the preceding decade must also be recognized since this work provided an understanding of the basic nature of gaming. In addition, related projects have been funded by the National Science Foundation, the National Institute of Mental Health, and the Department of Health, Education, and Welfare. The manuscript was completed while I was a fellow at the Netherlands Institute for Advanced Study in the Humanities and Social Sciences.

PREFACE

A decade ago, the term "gaming" did not exist in the popular lexicon. The literature of that period refers to it as "operational-gaming," a hyphenated adjunct to the newly developed field of operations-research. The term "gaming" first began to appear in a few academic papers, most notably those relating to business, political science and urban simulation. Today, it is common to find references to "gaming" almost daily in newspapers, national magazines, and a variety of other public and semi-public documents. The term "game," of course, has been in common use for centuries to mean a playful diversion or amusement.

The evolution of games from a form of play to a serious undertaking can be traced from war games in their earliest forms such as checkers and chess. By the eighteenth century, military games were in use for the analysis of possible real-world battle situations. By the advent of World War II, military games were no longer "play" and "gaming" was used to describe an activity of serious purpose. In the quarter century since World War II military gaming has become increasingly sophisticated; its importance to policymaking is evidenced by the secrecy associated with military gaming activities.

World War II spawned at least five developments

that have been woven into the fabric of gaming: computers, operations-research, the mathematical theory of games, simulation, and the early business games. "Gaming" for social science purposes did not emerge in its own right until the early 1960s; and the various gaming products of the ensuing decade reflect an initial confusion in its application.

The dramatic increase in the use of gaming in the last decade (see Figure 1) results both from the increased recognition of the technique's potential as well as from its diffusion through the social sciences for both academic and applied purposes. Its growth rate in the last several years has been explosive. Some critics suggest this may reflect a "fad"; more probably it indicates a very early point on a growth curve that will not begin to level out for at least a quarter century. As the true character of gaming as a unique communication form becomes clear, its use as a "*Future's Language*" will become pervasive.

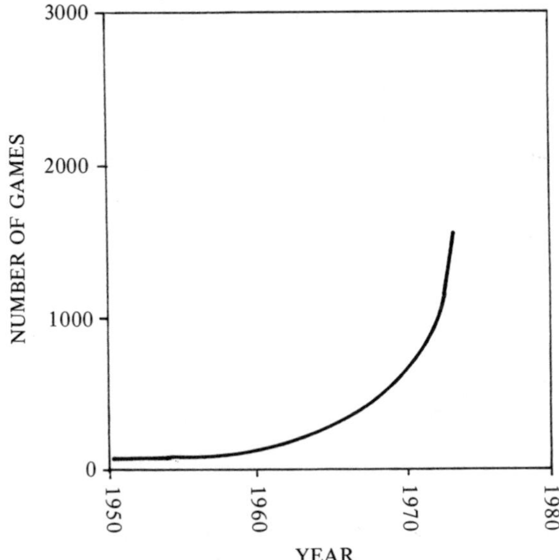

Note: There is considerable difficulty associated with developing such an estimate. These data have been derived from personal files accumulated since 1960; they tend to be confirmed by published sources (see Zuckerman & Horn, Newsletter, 1971).

While different sources offer different counts, the growth curve seems consistent as illustrated.

FIGURE 1.
Estimated Growth of Gaming/Simulation in the Social Sciences

The emergence of gaming professionalism is increasingly apparent. The National Gaming Council celebrated its tenth anniversary in 1971. Ten years earlier the group had been known as the East Coast War Games Council and during its ten year growth period had primarily represented both war and business games. In 1970 the International Simulation and Gaming Association was formed in Bad Godesburg, Germany; the year 1973 marked the first joint meeting of the National Gaming Council and the International Simulation and Gaming Association in Washington, D.C. Both groups have produced annual proceedings as well as occasional newsletters.

There is at least one professional journal, *Simulation and Games,* "an international journal of theory, design and research," published quarterly by Sage Publications since March 1970.[1] A fairly exhaustive bibliography on gaming related materials numbered only approximately 100 articles in 1964; a similar listing in 1973 contains over 2500 references, including many books. The literature has developed from the early "cookbooks" and descriptions of individual games to more sophisticated documents dealing with theory, design considerations, and evaluation of results. There is a wide variety of newsletters and periodicals, both commercial and academic, in circulation. The process of cataloguing, indexing, and reporting on games has now been formally undertaken in at least three instances, and one document has already been published in a revised edition.[2]

Centers of competence have emerged both in academic and other settings across the United States as well as in several other countries. However, a listing of any kind is hazardous because of the rapid development of new centers and the decline of some of the earlier ones. Nonetheless, there are several dozen such centers which range in structure and character from loose but productive coalitions of faculties at major universities to formally organized and reasonably well-funded centers. Virtually all universities now employ gaming in one academic context or another and courses dealing with gaming per se are commonplace. The content of these courses is continuing to shift from demonstrations of existing exercises to an investigation of the character and utility of gaming. In short, gaming was an embarrassment in most professional and academic contexts ten years ago. Today, it is being pursued in some very respectable places.

A major European country, upon the completion of an 18-month experiment in the use of gaming in an applied policy context, held a conference to evaluate the results. After several days of discussion it was apparent that the program had been reasonably successful and that games were becoming useful for some public policy purposes. In an effort to find an explanation for the success of the program, the evaluators asked an international group of experts for the delineation of the true character of gaming. Dissatisfied with the response, one distinguished government evaluator threw up his hands and said in exasperation, "It works! That's all we have!" This frustrated outburst is surely justified since to date there is no coherent theory which explains the phenomenon of gaming.

There are several perspectives from which gamers attempt to explain their product. These include:

(1) Systems exposition—an extension of operations-research that views the primary purpose of gaming as the representation of some complex system in abstract form, usually through simulation, in a man-machine interaction.

(2) Game-theoretical—an attempt to describe and understand games as an extension of the mathematical theory of games as initially expounded by Von Neumann and Morgenstern.

(3) Educational technique—the view that a game is a classroom technique, the modern equivalent of colored paper and paste.

(4) Correlation with societal process—an emphasis on role-playing and on the duplication of social interaction.

(5) Hyphenated disciplinary technique—political science-gaming, or war-gaming, or business-gaming or urban-gaming, or social-science-gaming, and so on.

(6) Crowd-pleasers—the widespread and sometimes indiscriminate use of games for the primary purpose of obtaining an enthusiastic player response.

Each of the perspectives has virtue in a given context. They do not, individually or in combination, provide a satisfactory perspective or explanation of gaming.

This confusion is fairly easily explained if one reviews the evolution of gaming technique. However, the lack of a coherent perspective on the character of gaming creates many problems. First, the potential user confronts a perplexing array of products without the assistance of interpretive criteria, and is forced to rely either on games which have become familiar through play or which may be recommended by colleagues. The various cataloguing efforts available are limited in usefulness because the discriptors employed are ambiguous and frequently result in a similarity in description of game products. This in no way belittles the heroic efforts of the cataloguers, but rather is an indication of the confused state of the gaming art, where clear ground rules do not yet exist. Until a valid generalized theory exists, meaningful descriptors cannot be developed and uniformly applied. Similarly, reasonable access to games is denied because of the lack of adequate libraries or clearinghouses which permit efficient search procedures. Once in use, a game may be difficult to evaluate; correspondingly, the development, design, and utilization of any given product may be inefficient because gamers tend to fumble through the process of game development instead of executing a design conceived before construction begins.

As a consequence, those who are forced to confront gaming from a policy level (whether or not a project should be funded, inclusion of gaming as part of an academic program, or use of the technique as an applied public policy tool) are left in an intellectual morass and must reach their decision on the basis of such criteria as past personal experiences with gaming, the credibility of the investigator (rather than the proposed project), or the enthusiasm of the prospective client.

This book, then, is an attempt to develop a unifying perspective on the nature of gaming and to do so in a context broad enough to include all serious gaming activity. Although no coherent theory has previously been compiled, there is some agreement, albeit somewhat intuitive, about what constitutes gaming activity. Figure 2 identifies available techniques along the two dimensions of rationality and calibration. This places gaming/simulation in relation to other techniques such as model building, systems analysis, or behavioral sciences within the quadrant described by "many variables," and distinguished from the other quadrants as relatively uncalibrated and intuitive. This book will deal with the set of techniques which falls within that quadrant, commonly called gaming/simulation, and will

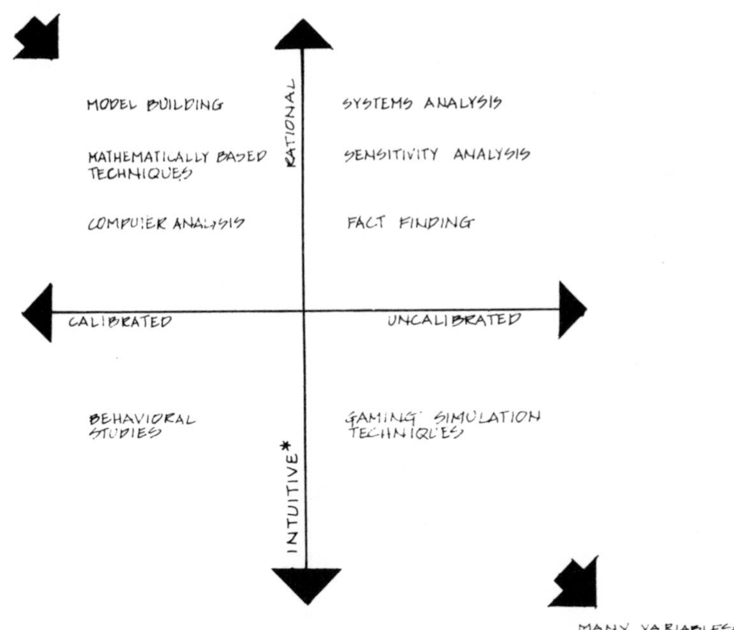

* The original diagram used rational-irrational for the vertical axis. We have substituted intuitive for irrational since this term seems to express better the character of gaming/simulation.

Source: R.H.R. Armstrong and Margaret Hobson, "ALEA Local Government Gaming Simulation Exercise," *Systems Behavior,* The Open University, Birmingham, 1973.

FIGURE 2.
Schematic Location of Gaming/Simulation

present its perspective in a format which will permit careful investigation and modification of the theory through time.

This effort flows from personal frustration resulting from the failure to generate any logical taxonomic structure worthy of presentation in a professional context. Like most professionals, my gaming efforts had been along rather limited lines, specifically urban simulation. Having completed an unwieldy, expensive, long-term gaming project which was successful beyond expectation, my curiosity made me take a second and more comprehensive look at gaming a decade after my first exposure.

A careful review of the variety of products currently available as serious games turned up the startling disclosure that they seem to share no single characteristic: neither subject matter nor technique, nor duration, nor client, nor audience configuration, nor paraphernalia, nor style. In one instance, the logic of math is illustrated by dice (wooden cubes) in an exercise requiring less than an hour; in another instance, a large and carefully trained staff, supplemented by a mammoth computer, confronts an audience of 50 to 100 people with an exercise of a week's duration. In one, role playing is emphasized, and in another, human decisionmaking is emphasized in an almost sterile man-machine context. A given exercise uses a board and the players move physical objects about in one instance; in another, visual aids are completely absent. Still another exercise closely mimics or simulates some real-world phenomenon, while another is a completely abstract phenomenon. Curiously, professionals have no difficulty in alluding to all of these as games, or addressing the phenomenon they use as "gaming" even though the particulars are so varied and diffuse.

On the assumption that several thousand professionals did, in fact, understand the phenomenon in practice even though the theory was not coherently expressed, I, deductively, set about in an effort to determine the nature of games. The process was slow, and entailed the identification of all terms or descriptors employed within the profession.[3] At the worst moment, over one thousand such terms had been identified. As the effort proceeded to organize these terms, a unifying perspective began to emerge—games are a form of communication.

The remaining sections of this book elaborate the thesis that gaming is a powerful new form of communication, particularly suited to conveying gestalt. The book attempts to explain the sudden, spontaneous, and widespread emergence of gaming as a result of fundamental societal changes now taking place. A theoretical base is presented which gives some insight into how gaming works; gaming as a language form, a Future's Language, is specified in detail; the theoretical statement is converted to pragmatic specifications for game design; and, finally, some speculations about the future of gaming are offered.

Because of the long-standing and widespread use of games, both definition and disclaimer are in order. The definition is postponed until Section II where a detailed statement is offered in a logical context. By way of disclaimer it must be noted that games are pervasive in society, both past and present.

They have long had the connotation of being an amusement or pastime, and they have frequently been acknowledged as the conveyors of folk wisdom. This book addresses a comparatively recent adaptation of this ancient skill for serious purpose in a disciplined manner—gaming/simulation or, for efficiency, gaming (these two terms are used interchangeably throughout the book). Further, it is assumed that the reader has experienced the play of a serious gaming/simulation exercise or will do so; the author does not believe the character of such an experience can be convincingly conveyed through prose.

In spite of this, some attempt to convey the character of a game seems in order, at least for the benefit of the uninitiated. Most of today's adult population will have played the parlor game *Monopoly* and can recall the excitement and intensity of play, even among adult participants. Visualize a similar experience with two significant modifications: first, the players are present because they share a desire to explore some problem; and second, the game is especially invented to facilitate discussion of that problem. It must be acknowledged that the particulars of format and technique, as well as content, will vary enormously. Nevertheless, the imagery conveyed by being a participant in an exciting game of Monopoly will give some idea of what occurs in a successful gaming/simulation.

Wassenaar, The Netherlands
March, 1974

NOTES

1. *Simulation and Games: An International Journal of Theory, Design, and Research* (Beverly Hills: Sage).

2. David W. Zuckerman and Robert E. Horn (eds.) *The Guide to Simulation/Games for Education and Training* (Lexington, Mass: Information Resources, Inc., P.O. Box 417, 1973).

3. Two conventions are used throughout the text: (1) all terms which are defined in the glossary are italicized at their first usage only; (2) all games mentioned in the text are cited in alphabetical order in the Appendix.

SECTION I

GESTALT

A structure or configuration of physical, biological, or psychological phenomena so integrated as to constitute a functional unit with properties not derivable from its parts in summation. *(Webster's Third New International Dictionary)*

1 THE PROBLEM

Humankind is a little harried of late. The naked ape barely blinked only to discover that his animal being has moved from the cave to the moon with little time for adjustment. It is difficult, perhaps impossible, to derive a valid "alienation index" for society; nonetheless, evidence exists that all is not right with Western civilization. The tune-out, drop-out syndrome is ever apparent, and even where enthusiasms are high and a genuine sense of urgency and responsibility exist there is pervasive frustration. The individual needs to be part of the processes affecting his life, but is currently devoid of effective means to join the dialogue about potential change.

This situation has grown more urgent because the problems of today are more complex, involving systems and interacting subsystems that go beyond normal human ken and which do not yield to conventional jargon or traditional forms of communication. In addition, the number of individuals who want to be effectively part of the dialogue is large and growing rapidly; there is a growing personal urgency because the solutions pursued today constitute a more pervasive intrusion in the individual's life. Man's struggle for the personal control of his life can be traced from the first limitations on the King's power as a result of the Magna Carta to the Declaration of Independence and the resulting constitutional governmental forms. Painfully won, these gains are now threatened by a technical aristocracy, the high priests of 1984. At the very moment when man seems to have finally garnered the power to control his personal destiny, he has been caught unaware in the grinding pincher movement of the complexity of societal survival in modern times and the inevitable technological response. This crunch has been on its way since the Industrial Revolution, but its rapid progression was precipitated by World War II. In particular, the spin-offs in computer technology, the resulting elaboration of the concept of "systems" and related evolving technologies have generated information networks beyond ready human comprehension. Management problems of modern Western society (and in a particular sense of the great urban centers) have created a modern equivalent of the biblical Tower of Babel. Now the high priests of technology speak only to the high priests of technology; God is dead, and the citizen, no matter how strongly motivated, can hardly get a word in edgewise.

Society's failure to respond to individual need is, in large part, a communication problem. The naked ape waved and grunted, and we do little better. Early forms of communication consisted of simple and highly sequential modes which sufficed in that non-complex environment. As society changed these communication modes grew correspondingly more sophisticated, but they remained essentially sequential. The naked, now harried, ape of today still employs these simple sequential tongues; but in a world several magnitudes more complex, these tongues leave him speechless. The highly constrained and sequential languages of the past and their related technologies (even in their highest forms) fail to convey gestalt, and so the complexity of today cannot be comprehended or communicated except with the greatest of effort, and then only by a new elite.

Consider our great urban centers as they exist today—multisystems within multisystems, alternative upon alternative presenting an incomprehensible, many-futured state which is being rearticulated daily—a great multifaceted sphere of complexity that cannot be managed, but must be. Management of such an environment requires a holistic perspective that cannot be obtained through traditional sequential communication forms.

Because of the lack of *gestalt communication* modes and therefore the lack of an integrated or holistic perspective, society's management of such complexity has consisted of four concurrent dimensions: false dichotomies, professional elitism, increasing dependency on technology, and gigantism. The inevitable, but false, dichotomies appear first: the bureaucrat pares out of the total fabric of society some element of great urgency, since he can neither understand nor solve the problem in its totality. But by attacking the problem piecemeal other evils are encountered, the least of which may be inefficiency, the most dangerous irrelevancy. As the bureaucracy transforms life into disconnected cells, programs often fail to achieve their purpose. Worse yet, the proposed solution may create problems which did not exist initially. These dichotomies breed the armies of a professional elite, and their empires and the resultant bureaucratic gigantism smother the citizen.

The solutions offered by these bureaucracies are often expressed as alternatives; these may seduce the man in the street, but the poor beggar in front of the bulldozer soon discovers the moment of truth. And as he turns into the jaws of this giant beast trying to locate some isolable component unit that will be responsive, he is put down by the elitest professional who quite literally speaks another language and he is put off by a technology that appears antihuman. His only alternative is to join together with fragmentary bands to throw slingshots at the giant. Occasionally, their aim is true! First one then another public scheme is beaten back not to be replaced with positive alternatives, but rather by frustrating standoffs allowing the great urban administrations to survive through nonaction. The creaking structure grinds on through time, the moans of unresolved needs and of endless counterproductive conflict emanating from the incongruous mass.

Is there any possibility, even among the elite, of establishing a real dialogue about this multifaceted dynamic gargantua? Is it possible to achieve positive management by substituting alternative future time frames to replace the negative reactionary reality? Is there any way to enlarge the dialogue to include the activist citizen or at least a "representative" who transmits a personal translation of ideas for his constituency? Not if we insist on restricting ourselves to the languages of the caveman.

But there is hope that the possibility for a quantum jump exists—that communication can move from its rigid and limiting sequentiality to a gestalt mode, and that this Future's Language can be used for simultaneous translation in our modern Tower of Babel.

FUTURE SHOCK

The situation just described results from a dramatic and fundamental change in societal structure over the past century; the change is permanent, irreversible, and more profound than any encountered before by mankind. This situation is most evident in the urbanized sector of the developed nations, and the less advanced societies will encounter even more precipitous change. This change requires no less of modern man than that he turn himself about—altering his institutions, himself, and his languages to permit thoughtful and rapid speculation about a many faceted future and to venture decisions where there is no precedent. Man no longer has the option of backing into the future, as our ancestors have done for unrecorded eons.

"Future Shock" has become part of the popular lexicon. In 1970 Alvin Toffler introduced the concept in a book by that name. He stressed the death of permanence and the coming of the age, not of Aquarius but of transience. His book documents in detail the thesis that the world of tomorrow will be significantly different from the world of yesterday along many dimensions. Toffler (1970: 15) quotes Kenneth Boulding: "the date that divides human history into two equal parts is well within living memory. . . . The world of today . . . is as different from the world in which I was born as that world was from Julius Caesar's."

Toffler divides the last 50,000 years of man's existence into life spans of 62 years. Of these, 650 were spent in caves.

> Only during the last 70 lifetimes has it been possible to communicate from one lifetime to another—as writing made it possible to do. Only during the last six lifetimes did masses of men ever see a printed word. Only during the last four has it been possible to measure time with any precision. Only in the last two has anyone anywhere used an electric motor. And the overwhelming majority of all the material goods we use in daily life today have been developed within the present, the 800th lifetime. (p. 15)

This 800th lifetime, our present time, makes life dramatically different for modern sophisticated man.

Toffler shows that many phenomena, such as urbanization, the use of energy, the availability of man-made goods and conveniences and the speed of transportation, if charted against a time axis, will reveal a long curve of very little slope turning abruptly upward within the last century. "The pattern, here and in a thousand other statistical series, is absolutely clear and unmistakable. Millennia go by, and then, in our own times, a sudden bursting of the limits, a fantastic spurt forward" (p. 26-27). Toffler attributes this change to a combination of technology and knowledge—technology makes change possible and knowledge becomes the fuel for technology. Toffler also emphasizes the profound changes in data and information available to modern man.

> Wave after wave of new images penetrate our defenses, shake up our mental models of reality. The result of this image bombardment is the accelerated decay of old images, a faster intellectual through-put, and a new, profound sense of the impermanence of knowledge, itself. . . . To maintain our adaptive balance . . . we struggle to refresh our imagery . . . relearn reality. . . . Our image-processing mechanisms . . . are driven to operate at higher and higher speeds. (p. 144, 160)

Figure 3 attempts to place these notions in perspective, vis-a-vis gaming. The horizontal axis represents centuries starting with the year zero. The vertical column represents an index of complexity, transience, and rate of change confronting the typical citizen. Using a logarithmic scale, a curve is plotted

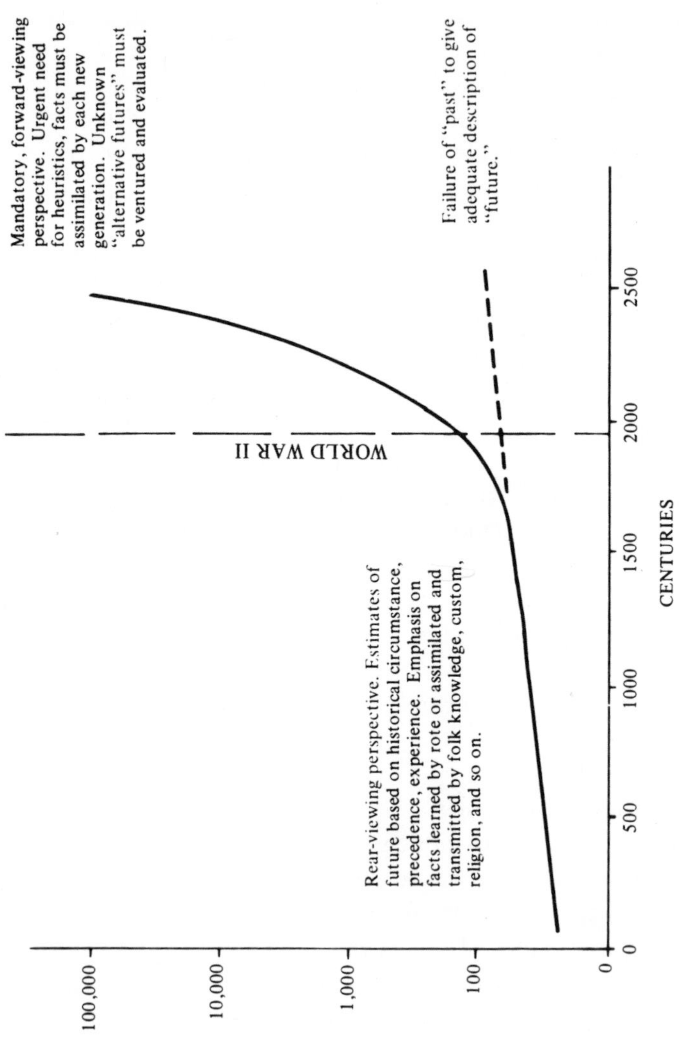

FIGURE 3.
Societal Complexity

which attempts to illustrate this change (perhaps the number of new things which must be assimilated in the lifetime of a given citizen). The curve starts in the lower left hand corner as a straight line with a slight upward incline, until perhaps 1900. The curve turns vertically during the period 1900 to 1940 with a sharp increase during the period of World War II. After World War II the curve is increasing at a nearly vertical rate as change flows on change at a totally unprecedented rate. The pattern over the centuries preceding the industrial revolution was fairly consistent. Daily life was largely governed by precedent, and changes evolved slowly. The basic perspective was rear-viewing; information was either acquired by rote or transmitted by folk knowledge, custom or religion.

Since World War II, it has become mandatory to develop a future-oriented perspective. There is an urgent need for information assimilated as heuristics rather than fact since the recurrent waves of new "facts" are too numerous and too fleeting in duration to be captured and assimilated by each new generation. Alternative futures must be advanced and selected, frequently where no useful precedent exists. Traditional modes of communication do not lend themselves to transmitting heuristics. We must devise new modes which are more effective at providing overview.

INADEQUACY OF LANGUAGE FORMS

The need for conveying holistic thought, or *gestalt,* is urgent, and the coming decade will increase this urgency considerably as new information is generated exponentially and the problems of the world grow more complex. Perhaps the most trenchant statement on this need is by R. F. Rhyne (1973):

> There is a macro-problem, an interweaving of adverse conditions that is more extensive, more richly structured by interior lines of interaction, and more threatening than any circumstance faced before by all mankind. (p. 93)

Rhyne's purpose was "to stimulate exploration of the means whereby appreciations of complex wholes may be more quickly and more reliable told to others." He rejects our ancestral language forms as inadequate to the task and argues that new forms must be invented. Arguing that decision is a gestalt event and not a logically determinable process, he believes that the citizen, the policy researcher or other decisionmaker must first comprehend the whole—the entirely, the gestalt, the system—before the particulars can be dealt with.

Man thinks in images, in a gestalt. He transmits his images to others by means of language—but this requires that he translate his holistic image into a sequential string of component descriptions, and that his listener attempt to reconstruct the image—"a picture is worth a thousand words." Sequentiality is sufficient as long as the listener can hold initial components while he receives later ones; this requires that the gestalt be simple. Because a mental holding process breaks down very quickly under the strain of today's complexity, another method of transmitting information must be developed.

Language in the past has performed basically one of two purposes: it was either a pragmatic means for the common man to transmit to his neighbor the essentials of day-to-day life or it was a mode of communication among a sophisticated elite used to maintain themselves in power. We now need to find a vehicle of communication which better permits us to comprehend the future, and which permits more intelligent dialogue about complexity by larger percentages of mankind. It is now apparent that man must deal not with *a* future but with *many* futures; and we are not very well equipped to think these through with the languages historically available to us.

Language has as one of its strongest components the use of analogy. Through analogy we are able to modify associations derived from past phenomena. Mankind must now develop analogies which are based upon pure conjecture, but which can be used to formulate hypotheses about the future. In short, we must learn to reminisce about the future, thoughtfully, carefully, and in realistic detail if we are to select that future which best serves mankind.

Necessity is the mother of invention, and the post-

World War II period has produced many innovations in communications which attempt to deal with this increased complexity. Each reflects an attempt to convey gestalt, or at least to escape from the harsh burden of strict sequentiality of written and spoken language. When plotted on a graph, the curve of developed games (Figure 1) mimics rather accurately the curve of accelerated change (Figure 3) with perhaps a ten year lag. Gaming is a spontaneous solution by many people in many situations to the problem of developing a gestalt communication form—they have developed a new language, a form which is "future" oriented. Such a perspective begins to explain the wide diversity of materials which appear as games; it becomes a useful guide to the development of effective games. This development of the gaming/simulation technique offers extraordinary opportunity for sophisticated and rapid communication; it will permit man to cope with the inevitable kaleidoscope of new imagery which he must confront.

SUMMARY

The central thesis of this book, then, is that gaming is a "Future's Language," a new form of communication emerging suddenly and with great impact across many lands and in many problem situations. This new communication form represents the first effort by man to formulate a language which is oriented to the future. This future will in all certainty differ dramatically from the past, and the languages which have passed to us from antiquity will no longer suffice. The problems which must be faced in the future differ from those of the past because of their relative complexity, the rapidity of their occurrence, the newness of their character, and the systemic origin of the basic problems involved. Gaming/simulation is a hybrid communication form. It is new, not well understood, poorly used, and in its infancy. Nonetheless, there is convincing evidence that when it is treated with the same precision and understanding as traditional forms of communication it will prove to be very useful to man in the approaching decades.

SECTION II

INTRODUCTION TO SECTION II

To establish the characteristics that are peculiar to gaming/simulation as a communication form, and thereby gain insight into the efficient use of this mode of communication, it is first necessary to review the characteristics of alternative modes of communication.

In this section, a *communication mode* is defined as the integrated use of *language, communications technology,* and the *patterns of interaction* of the respondents. Examples of different modes of communication are introduced; these are arrayed along a continuum to emphasize their unique features and limiting characteristics. This continuum is then analyzed in terms of the three mode components (language, patterns of interaction, and communications technology) to illustrate the changes which take place as we move along the continuum from simple to complex modes. The major groupings of communication modes are then defined in terms of several central characteristics: the ability to convey gestalt, the range of subject matter which can be dealt with, the ease of usage, the ease with which the form can be changed while in use, the range of audience that can be accommodated, and the characteristics of the message which can be conveyed. Special attention is given to the integrated communication modes and a new mode, Future's

Language, is defined and examples are cited. Gaming/simulation is introduced, but a full statement is deferred until after an explanation is offered as to how these different modes of communication work.

Having defined *what* communication modes are, an attempt is made to illustrate *how* these work by offering four rudimentary models of human communication. These illustrate, with progressive complexity, the four major categories along the communication continuum; each model attempts to illustrate the character of the three mode components and their integration as the communication mode becomes more sophisticated. A fifth model which further elaborates on communication through gaming simulation is presented after a discussion of gaming as a Future's Language. The unique ability of gaming/simulation to convey the gestalt of complex systems is described, and gaming/simulation is defined. Finally, some thoughts are offered on how we learn through gaming/simulation.

2 MODES OF HUMAN COMMUNICATION

Before attempting a definition of gaming/simulation in a communication context, it is necessary to review some of the central characteristics of the various forms of human communication. There is an abundance of modes of communication; a few of these have been selected and arrayed along a "communication continuum" (Figure 4). These are presented in three groups: (1) primitive (those which are most simple, not necessarily restricted to those of remote origins); (2) advanced (a series of sophisticated forms of communication which can be used independently of one another); and (3) integrated forms (those which entail the coordinated usage of two or more of the "advanced" forms for special purposes).

Primitive forms of communication fall into both informal (grunts, hand signals) and formal modes (semaphores, navigational lights). In both instances they are ubiquitous. Hand signals and body language can be used to locate a toilet in any country; "international" road signs employing standard signals are finding their way into formal usage throughout the world. In spite of this basic universality, these "primitive" modes can only be used to convey relatively simple messages.

EXAMPLES		
GRUNTS HAND SIGNALS	INFORMAL	PRIMITIVE
SEMAPHORE LIGHTS FLAGS	FORMAL	PRIMITIVE
CONVERSATION LECTURE SEMINAR	SPOKEN	ADVANCED
TELEGRAM LETTER BOOK	WRITTEN	ADVANCED
MATHEMATICAL AND MUSICAL NOTATION SCHEMATICS	TECHNICAL	ADVANCED
ACTING ART ROLE PLAYING	ARTISTIC	ADVANCED
FILM TELEVISION	MULTI-MEDIA	INTEGRATED
FLOW CHART HIGHWAY MAP	FUTURE'S LANGUAGE	INTEGRATED
ICONIC MODELS ARCHITECTURAL SCALE MODEL	FUTURE'S LANGUAGE	INTEGRATED
GAMING/SIMULATION	FUTURE'S LANGUAGE	INTEGRATED

FIGURE 4.
A Communication Continuum

Advanced forms of communication abound, but four types are presented to illustrate their general character: spoken or verbal communication (conversations, lectures); written messages (books, letters); technical forms (mathematical or musical notation, advanced forms of schematic representations such as blueprints); and artistic modes (painting, sculpture, acting). A given advanced communication mode is more specialized than any given primitive form. English is of little value in the heart of Mexico; the computer language "Fortran" is of value only among those with the necessary technical training. But in the proper setting these advanced forms can be used to transmit complex messages.

Integrated forms of communication result from man's efforts to go beyond the limitations of the various individual "advanced" modes. They are described here in two forms, multimedia (slides coordinated with a lecture, movies, television) and Future's Language (see Chapter 4 for a complete definition). The use of integrated forms of communication flows from special needs not successfully met by the "advanced" forms individually employed; the effort to "integrate" always entails more cost and effort. Integrated forms can be employed to convey very elaborate messages with special nuance. Inevitably, a given usage has very specific limits of application. Movies may be developed for many different subjects; however, a given movie will be of value in only certain instances.

Of course, this presentation of the "communication continuum" is simplified. Hopefully, it will meet our purpose—that is, to give some perspective on gaming/simulation as a mode of communication.

COMMUNICATION MODES

Any given mode of communication is composed of three components: language, pattern of interaction among the respondents, and communication technology (see Figure 5). The transmission of any message entails the use of a language, defined for our purposes as a symbol-set, and the conventions governing its use. A language may be standardized and in conventional use (English, mathematics), or it may be specially created for a restricted situation. Professionals develop a jargon for use within a given field (law, medicine), and in the vernacular a layman might say that they "speak a language of their own." This problem-specific jargon occurs naturally during gaming events. If the game designer prepares properly for the jargon, it can facilitate good communication during the game.

The structure of a language may not be readily apparent or formalized; typically, the user will be unknowingly trained in the use of these "rules" (see Figure 6)—to learn such a rule structure is an intellectual exercise distinct from the operational use of a language. As a consequence, most of the

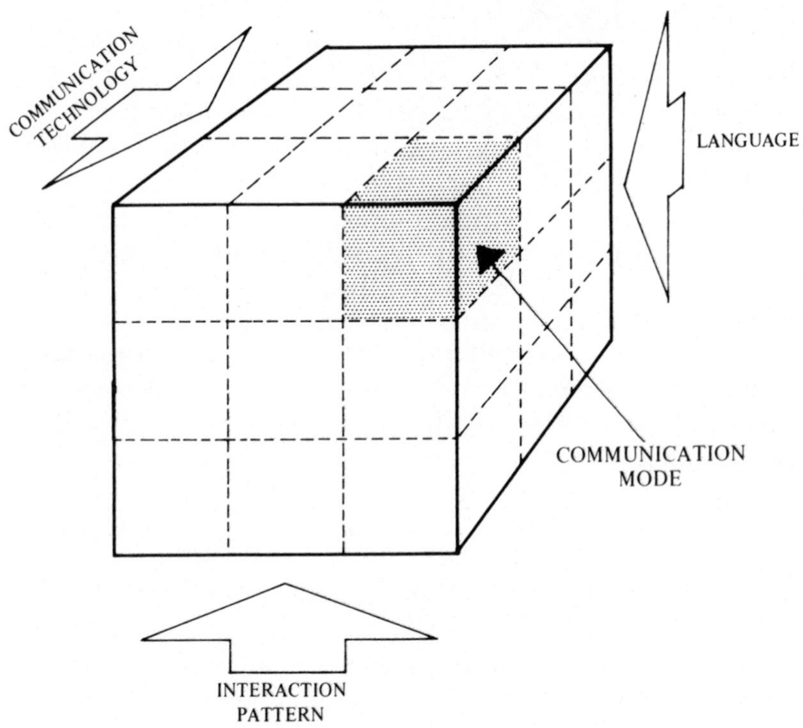

FIGURE 5.
A Communication Mode

"My boy, Grand-père is not the one to ask about such things. I have lived eighty-seven peaceful and happy years in Montoire-sur-le-Loir without the past anterior verb form."

SOURCE: *New Yorker Magazine,* Vol. 49, No. 26, page 27 (August 20, 1973).

FIGURE 6.

The Unconscious Use of Grammatical Rules

population of the world learns and uses their language without being consciously aware of its structure. This phenomenon exists in games where participants are confronted by a *game-specific language* which they learn, use, and discard without having been intellectually aware of the process.

Communication technology is defined here to include both natural and man-made devices for transmitting a message from sender(s) to receiver(s). Natural phenomena (the human larynx and ear) are frequently coupled with artificial devices (printing, telephone, film, slide projection equipment, and so on). The more complex the method, the more specialized the communications situation and the more likely that natural phenomena will be supplemented by man-made devices in increasingly sophisticated configurations.

Patterns of interaction among respondents also vary

from the simple to the complex (see Figure 7). The simplest forms are two-person exchanges, in either one-way or two-way *dialogue* exchanges. Multi-person exchanges become more involved. While there are many possible patterns of interaction in multi-person exchanges, two forms are germane here: sequential dialogue and multilogue. *Sequential dialogue* has been selected to represent the pattern between a central figure (lecturer or speaker) and an audience. This pattern is found in conference sessions, classrooms, public meetings, technical sessions, and so on, and is the most common and presumably

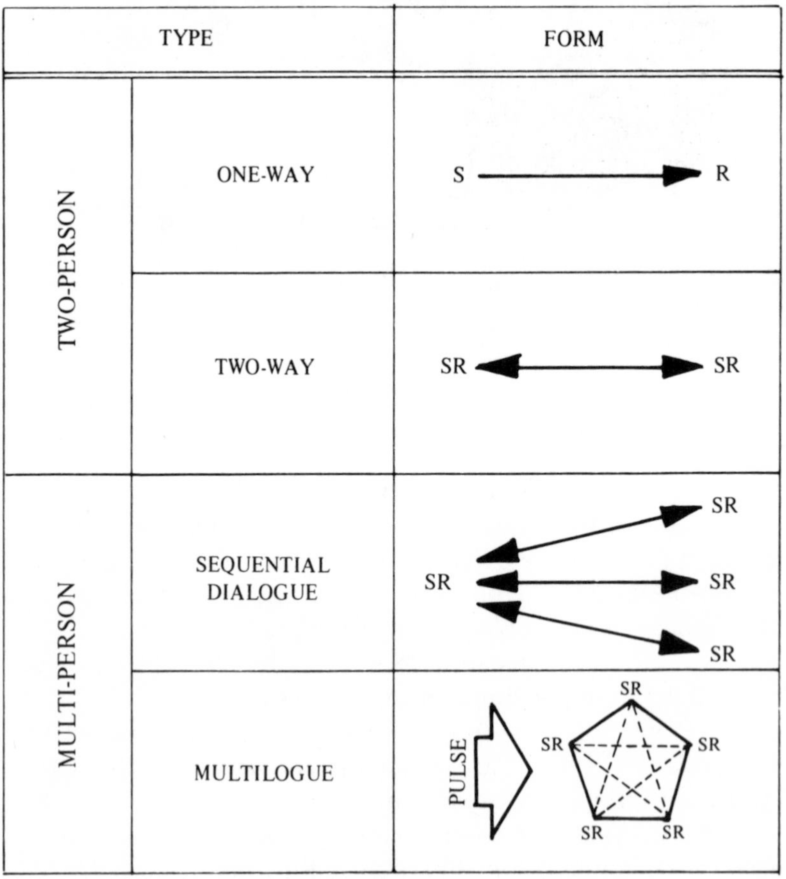

TYPE		FORM
TWO-PERSON	ONE-WAY	S → R
	TWO-WAY	SR ↔ SR
MULTI-PERSON	SEQUENTIAL DIALOGUE	SR ↔ SR SR ↔ SR SR ↔ SR
	MULTILOGUE	PULSE; SR, SR, SR, SR, SR (all interconnected)

S = Sender, R = Receiver, SR = Sender/Receiver.

FIGURE 7.
Patterns of Interaction

the most efficient pattern. It is used to exchange ideas or information focused on some area of interest by a group varying in size from less than 10 to more than 100 persons. It is characterized by an initial statement by a central figure followed by a series of remarks from respondents which are directed back to the leader of the meeting (comments directly between the respondents are usually prohibited). The leader may present his information in its entirety before the discussion, or may present it in a series of logical units interspersed with questions/answers and comments.

The other pattern, *multilogue* (multiple, simultaneous dialogue), is perhaps less common, but very productive. This implies that a group is focused on a single communication objective (*pulse*); this direction is simultaneously pursued through dialogue by random correspondents, each exchange representing a different perspective on the problem at hand. Such exchange is likely to be followed by a more orderly "wrap-up" session developed along the lines of the third pattern of "sequential dialogue." Multilogue occurs quite naturally in some small group situations. It is frequently deliberately contrived as counterpoint to a lecture in a formal conference session (following a presentation, the attendees are broken up into small "discussion groups," typically five to seven persons, and subsequently returned to the original conference format). Multilogue is the primary interaction pattern in gaming/simulation. This pattern properly coordinated with the other technique is central to the game's ability to display gestalt.

In summary, man employs a variety of communication modes. These may be perceived as falling along a continuum and ranging from the simple to the complex. As they become more complex, their three basic components—language, communication technology, and pattern of interaction—become more sophisticated and complex both individually and in their combined patterns (see Figure 8). Gaming/simulation is at the most sophisticated end of the continuum, and typically employs multiple languages (including a game-specific language), multilogue, and a sophisticated, interactive combination of communication technologies.

MODES / COMPONENTS	PRIMITIVE	ADVANCED	INTEGRATED	
			MULTIMEDIA	FUTURE'S LANGUAGE
LANGUAGE	Few symbols Simple conventions	Many symbols Complex conventions	Multiple sets of symbols; Parallel complex conventions	Multiple sets of symbols; Some newly created; Parallel, complex situation-specific conventions
PATTERNS OF INTERACTION	One-way Two-way	One-way Two-way Multiple Dialogue	One-way Two-way Multiple Dialogue	One-way Two-way Multiple Dialogue Multilogue
COMMUNICATION TECHNOLOGY	Few, Simple	Many, Complex	Sophisticated combinations	Sophisticated combinations Interactive

FIGURE 8.
The Components of Communication Modes

CHARACTERISTICS OF COMMUNICATION MODES

Man's communication needs are infinitely varied, and, consequently, many formats are employed. To better understand the unique function of the major types of modes, several common characteristics have been identified. These characteristics vary across the communication continuum. The six characteristics are defined below:

1. *Sequential/gestalt constraint*—the inherent ability of the communications mode to convey gestalt or holistic imagery.
2. *Universality/specificity*—the degree of flexibility inherent to the language form in adapting to new substantive material.
3. *Spontaneity of use*—the ease or relative freedom with which a user can employ a given mode.
4. *Mutability*—the ability of the communications mode to be altered while in use.
5. *Range (catholicity)*—the range of audience who can employ the mode.
6. *Message characteristics*—the success with which a number of message characteristics can be conveyed, including but not limited to complexity, analogy, qualitative thought, quantitative thought, subtlety, permanency, precision, intangibles, time constraints, and system characteristics.

These characteristics have been selected because of their particular relevance to gaming/simulation. To further clarify their meaning, they are described in more detail below.

Sequential/Gestalt

Sequential communication exists in all communication modes to some extent, and inhibits the transmission of some types of messages. As we move to the right along the continuum (see Figure 9) a variety of devices are employed to ease this constraint. For example, in the primitive mode employ-

MODES / CHARACTERISTICS	PRIMITIVE		ADVANCED				INTEGRATED	
	INFORMAL	FORMAL	SPOKEN	WRITTEN	TECHNICAL	ARTISTIC	MULTIMEDIA	FUTURE'S LANGUAGE
SEQUENTIAL/ GESTALT	Highly sequential.		Basically sequential but various devices employed to ease this constraint.				Least sequential; most capable of conveying gestalt.	
UNIVERSALITY/ SPECIFICITY	May be employed for a broad array of subject matter.		Standardized modes suitable for in-depth usage with a limited range of applications.				Mode specifically tailored to a communication need.	
SPONTANEITY	Natural, easy, convenient.		Special skills required. Sophisticated uses often "dry."				Special effort required to initiate these. Spontaneous in usage.	
MUTABILITY	Readily adaptable to the situation at hand.		Formalized structures; changes evolve slowly.				Specialized constructs adapted to special situation; often can be adapted while in use.	
RANGE (CATHOLICITY)	May be employed by a broad range of people.		Application limited to those skilled in a particular mode.				When carefully constructed, suitable for a diverse clientele.	
MESSAGE CHARACTERISTICS	Only rudimentary message can be conveyed.		Sophisticated messages can be conveyed.				Can convey sophisticated message in a gestalt context.	

FIGURE 9.
Characteristics of Communication Modes

ing semaphore flags, the message recipient is required to accept the symbols one by one, and can only interpret the message after a logical string of symbols has been received. Contrast this with written English, where the reader can skip forward in the text at will, and is normally aided in comprehending the meaning and significance of a particular passage by a variety of stylistic conventions (table of contents, sections, chapters, paragraphs, schematic material to illustrate the *linkage* of ideas). In spite of these devices, the basic sequentiality of a book is very pronounced. Letter follows letter to make words, words string into sentences, and so on.

Selecting a more technical mode further along the continuum, such as flow-charting, we discover greater freedom in conveying gestalt. The user of a flow chart can, to some extent, select his own route through the structure, and is also permitted to double back and select alternate paths. A flow chart is a "picture" of a certain logical set, and although its inherent sequentiality is still evident (if condition "X," go to box 36) it is particularly valuable for conveying the logic of a "system."

The primary motivation for the development of the various integrated communication modes is to increase the ability to convey gestalt, to escape the cumbersome sequentiality of simple modes. Contrast the imagery transmitted by a film abstracted from a Russian novel with that derived from a reading of the text. The text will certainly give more detailed information, but even the most diligent of readers, buffered by a detailed logical mapping of the emerging developments, cannot as quickly obtain the sweeping overview provided by the film.

There are good reasons for the wide diversity of communication modes. One is not necessarily "better" than another, but certainly one is often more *appropriate* than another. It is particularly important to establish that gaming/simulation is appropriate to a given situation before embarking on its use. Gaming/simulation has a very high capability for conveying gestalt, or holistic imagery.

Universality/Specificity

As one moves to the right along the continuum of communication modes, each particular mode becomes more subject-specific, and, therefore, less suitable for a broad array of purposes. The various forms of communication suggested under the integrated modes are elaborate constructs devised to meet highly specific communications objectives. Gaming/simulation is located to the extreme right of the continuum because each given product employs a specially contrived jargon (game-specific language).

Some communication modes are "frames" into which content must be added. For example, flow charts or crossword puzzles may be suitable as techniques for a wide array of content. Once the content has been added the product can only be employed for a limited usage. There are numerous *frame games* which meet this description.

Spontaneity

The ease of use of the various modes of communication ranges from the spontaneous cry of warning to the technological jungle associated with a television or movie production. In the latter instances, the creation of the specific mode (film, videotape) may be very complicated; however, the completed product may be quite simple to employ (reading a book versus writing and publishing it). Note that the spontaneity of use of games will vary tremendously; it is a function of the techniques and the design skill employed.

Mutability

There is a very broad diversity among the various communication forms in terms of the user's ability to change them. To the extent that a pattern exists along the continuum it is more nearly bell-shaped than continuous. For example, the most simple modes have little formal structure and can change upon the agreement of the two corresponding parties. Written English follows certain formalized conventions, but even these yield through time. The more precise technical forms are even more resistant to the whimsy of the user; mathematics, musical notation, and computer programming languages derive their great value in part from their relative constancy. To the extent they are directed toward a passive receiver, the more sophisticated forms such as books and films are essentially immutable in any given instance; a given family (films) will change readily through time. Gaming/simulation as a communication form employs active sender/receivers, and as a consequence a specific game can be altered while in use.

Range of use

The relative catholicity of the various communication modes, like the characteristic of mutability, must be perceived as somewhat bell-shaped; that is, those at either end of the continuum will find a greater array of potential users. Everyone can grunt or point and most adults, even the illiterate, can participate successfully in a serious game situation. The advanced modes in the center of the continuum inevitably are restricted to those with the necessary specialized skills (reading, writing, mathematics, and so on). Each gaming/simulation is a special construct for a given purpose; to be successful, the primary audience must be defined before construction begins.

Message Characteristics

In general, the more primitive the mode, the more rudimentary the message conveyed. As communication needs become more sophisticated, distinct message characteristics emerge which influence the mode of communication selected. Emotional messages may be presented through the various art forms; highly precise and/or theoretical constructs may rely more heavily on mathematical notation than English prose. If there is a strong need to convey a sophisticated message in a gestalt context, an integrated mode will be selected. Because games are specifically constructed for a particular communication problem the individual game construct will take a unique form—only then can the idiosyncratic needs of conveying the message be satisfied.

To summarize, there are several characteristics which can be used to analyze the various modes of communication and which help to explain the character and special utility of gaming/simulation; these relationships are abstracted in Figure 10. All along the continuum the function of each mode is message transmission, but as this message becomes more involved, abstract, and sophisticated a price must be paid. As we move to the right along the continuum the modes become more difficult and expensive to employ, but there is a corresponding gain in overcoming perceptual difficulties.

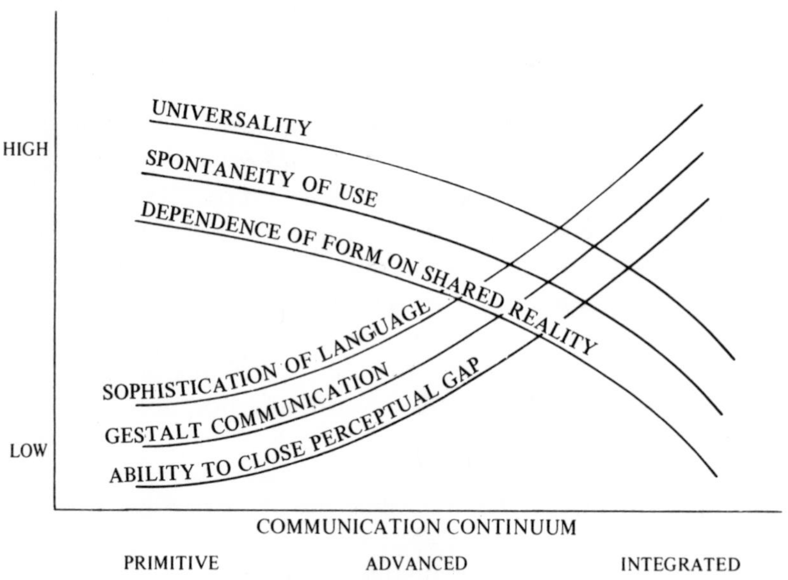

FIGURE 10.
Variation of Mode Characteristics

3 MODELS OF HUMAN COMMUNICATION

In order to best illustrate the character of the communication process during the use of a gaming/simulation, four models have been prepared. The four models (see Figure 11) include primitive one-way communication, dialogue in an advanced mode, multi-person dialogue, and multiple simultaneous dialogue (multilogue). These representations are presented as essentially static, although the processes they represent are certainly not. An attempt to show "multilogue" as a dynamic process occurring during a game event is reserved until the next chapter. All of the models are simplistic; further detail has been forsaken in the interest of focusing on a model of communication which is oriented toward communicating holistic insight.

The models (Figure 11) represent abstractions of four distinct modes of communication. As such, each contains the three components of language, interaction pattern, and communications technology. The models focus primarily on patterns of interaction, which is a critical aspect of gaming.

EXAMPLES / COMPONENTS	1	2	3	4
	PRIMITIVE	ADVANCED	INTEGRATED	
			MULTIMEDIA	FUTURE'S LANGUAGE
	SIMPLE ONE-WAY COMMUNICATION	TELEPHONE CONVERSATION	MULTI-PERSON SEQUENTIAL DIALOGUE	COMMUNICATION THRU GAMING/SIMULATION
LANGUAGE	Sign language Grunts	Spoken English	Spoken English with visuals	English, math, game-specific language
PATTERN	One-way	Two-way (Dialogue)	Multi-person Sequential dialogue	Multilogue (Multi-person simultaneous dialogue)
COMMUNICATION TECHNOLOGY	Larnyx Sound waves Ear	Telephone system	Voice, microphone Slide projector	Voice Phone Telephone Wall charts
EXAMPLE OF MESSAGE	Come here!	Can you come tomorrow if it does not rain?	Discussion of impact on a community of ethnic group in-migration	Discussion of impact on a community of ethnic group in-migration

FIGURE 11.
Four Models of Human Communication

MODEL NO. 1

The first model portrays a rudimentary one-way communication (see Figure 12). While such a format may be primitive, the content need not be inconsequential (Paul Revere's famous midnight ride was prompted by a simple code of lights— "one if by land, two if by sea"). At this stage, the pattern is quite simple, from sender to receiver; the two are easily distinguishable because a response (dialogue) is precluded by the format. A language is employed as a device for encoding the sender's idea or message; the receiver must know the same language in order to comprehend the message (decode it). At this level, the message may be transmitted entirely by natural phenomena (the larynx and the ear), or an artificial technology may be employed (a bullhorn to amplify voice in a crowd).

MODEL NO. 2

The second model (see Figure 13) represents a very common pattern of human conversation, in this case transmitted by telephone. Both parties are sender/receiver, speaking the same language. The form is highly sequential, word following word, until the speaker comes to a natural pause or is interrupted by his correspondent. Dialogue, then, is defined for our purposes as an interrupted serial message, alternating in direction. The introduction of this give-and-take format is important because it permits improved comprehension of complex messages. The respondents can, within certain bounds, explore nuance, establish context for an idea, and go forward or backward into the "message" as may be required. Contrast this with the pattern of a respondent listening to a formal lecture; if a point is missed as the message stream is presented, there is no immediate opportunity for clarification. This may result in a failure to comprehend subsequent points in the flow of information from the lecturer.

In this instance we have selected the telephone as the communication technology employed. A communication

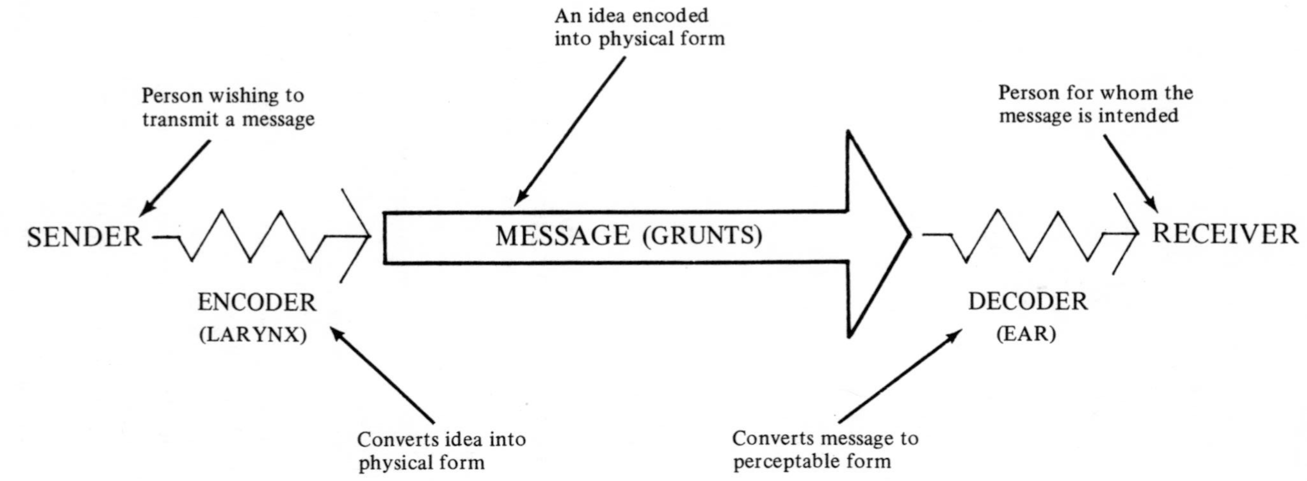

FIGURE 12.
Model No. 1: Primitive Communication

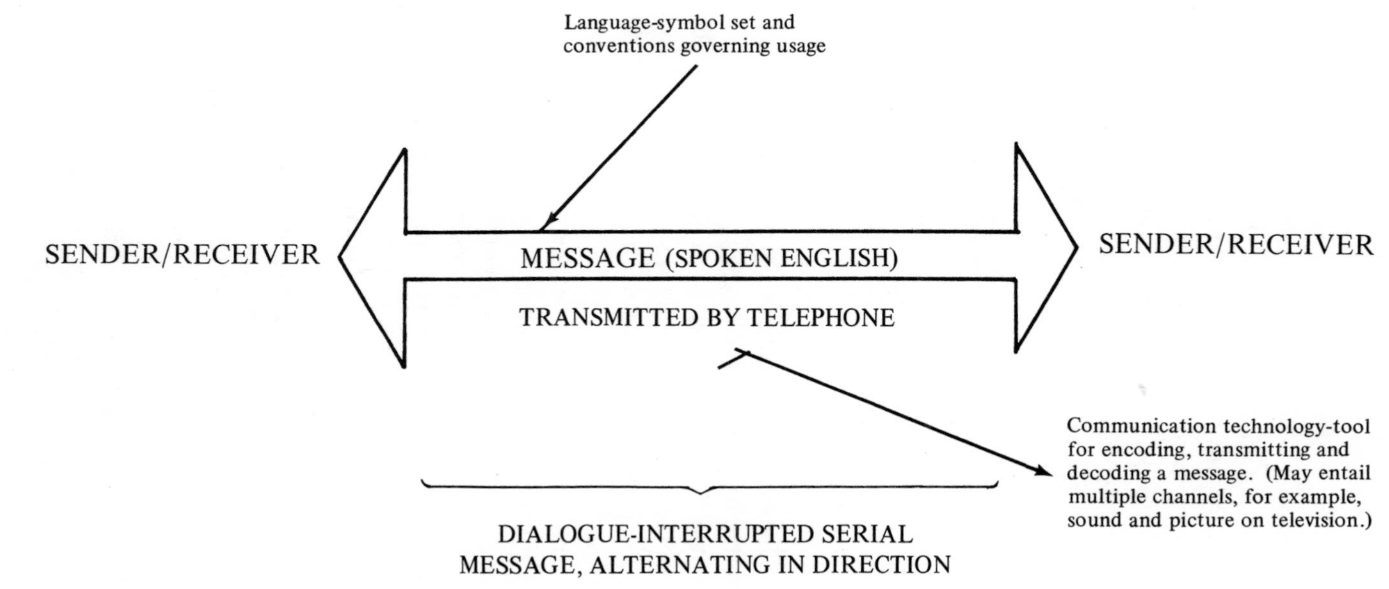

FIGURE 13.
Model No. 2: Advanced Communication

technology is defined as a tool for encoding, transmitting, and decoding a message; these may be quite elaborate, with multiple synchronized channels as in the use of television or film. Communication technology may be employed in various elaborate formats to assist in conveying complex messages; often this requires that the recipient be passive. The language employed in this example is spoken English. Because the interaction is two-way, the sender/receiver may employ any modification comprehensible to both parties (colloquialism, jargon)—there is no requirement to adhere to an outside standard. As the number of respondents increases (multiple sequential dialogue) the need for standardization becomes more imperative.

MODEL NO. 3

The standard lecture or conference format (multi-person sequential dialogue) has been selected both because it is common and it highlights the need for a gestalt mode to convey some types of messages. This model is somewhat more involved than the first two and necessitates elaboration of some additional concepts.

The most significant change from the first two models is the introduction of a more complex message. In this new model (see Figure 14) we seek a communication mode which is suitable for topics which are multifaceted, obscure in some dimensions, highly abstract, predicated on theoretical constructs subject to varying interpretation from differing perspectives, tentative and changing as new information is brought to bear, and possessed of complex structural relationships with significant linkages between the various components.

Model No. 3 introduces the concept of a *complex reality* as the subject for discussion in the typical lecture or conference mode. There are several impediments to the discussion of a serious topic in this context, stemming both from the problems of perceiving and transmitting complexity, as well as from the mechanical aspects of engaging a group of people in the dialogue. In the first instance, a complex topic must be

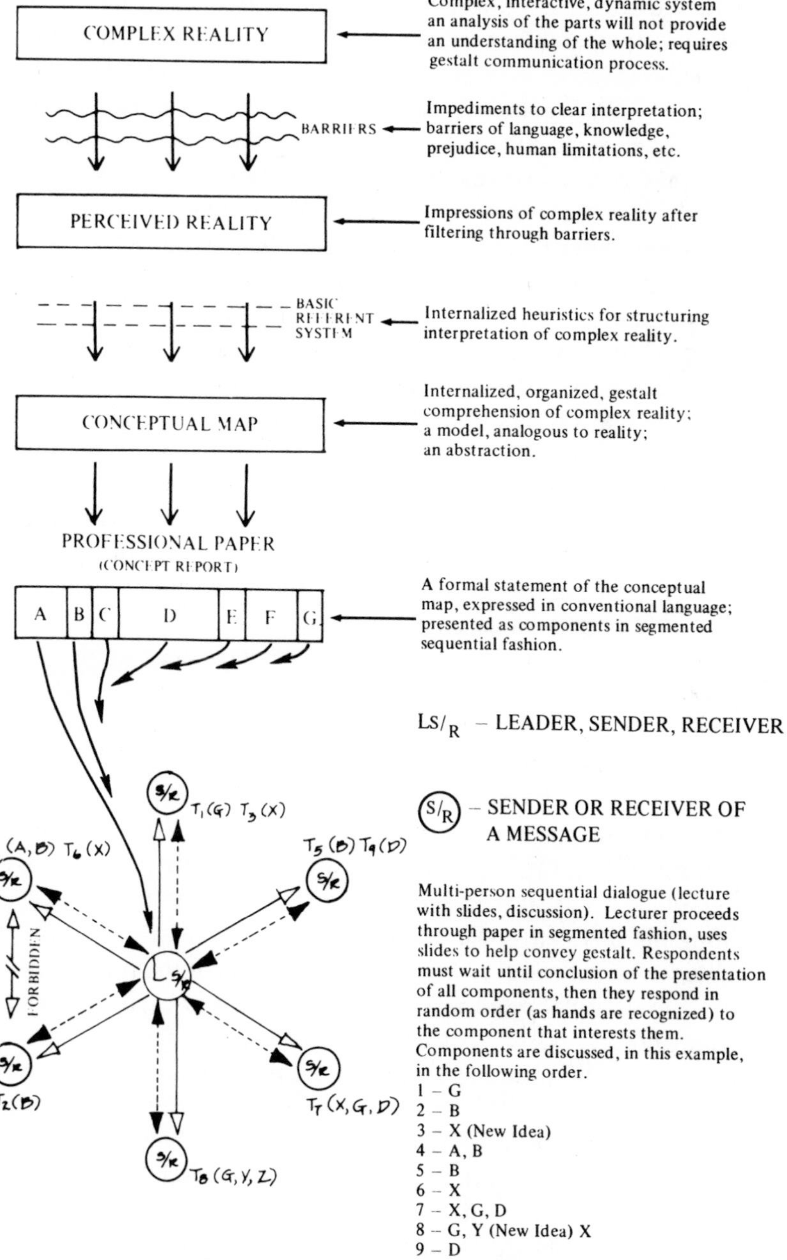

COMPLEX REALITY
Complex, interactive, dynamic system an analysis of the parts will not provide an understanding of the whole; requires gestalt communication process.
BARRIERS
Impediments to clear interpretation; barriers of language, knowledge, prejudice, human limitations, etc.
PERCEIVED REALITY
Impressions of complex reality after filtering through barriers.
BASIC REFERENT SYSTEM
Internalized heuristics for structuring interpretation of complex reality.
CONCEPTUAL MAP
Internalized, organized, gestalt comprehension of complex reality; a model, analogous to reality; an abstraction.
PROFESSIONAL PAPER
(CONCEPT REPORT)
A
B
C
D
E
F
G
A formal statement of the conceptual map, expressed in conventional language; presented as components in segmented sequential fashion.
LS/R – LEADER, SENDER, RECEIVER
S/R – SENDER OR RECEIVER OF A MESSAGE
T1 (G) T3 (X)
T4 (A, B) T6 (X)
T5 (B) T9 (D)
FORBIDDEN
T2 (B)
T7 (X, G, D)
T8 (G, Y, Z)
Multi-person sequential dialogue (lecture with slides, discussion). Lecturer proceeds through paper in segmented fashion, uses slides to help convey gestalt. Respondents must wait until conclusion of the presentation of all components, then they respond in random order (as hands are recognized) to the component that interests them. Components are discussed, in this example, in the following order.
1 – G
2 – B
3 – X (New Idea)
4 – A, B
5 – B
6 – X
7 – X, G, D
8 – G, Y (New Idea) X
9 – D

FIGURE 14.
Model No. 3: Integrated-Multimedia Multi-Person Sequential Dialogue

abstracted to a manageable level and committed to some trial statement (preferably written) which serves as a basis for discussion.

In Figure 14, we start with a complex reality that is all of one fabric, albeit its pattern is partially obscure; nonetheless, the process of abstracting and organizing inevitably results in a segmented presentation to the receivers. The choice of the term "complex reality" deliberately suggests a problem whose dimensions cannot readily be grasped in their entirety by human faculties. *Barriers* to complete and unambiguous understanding of reality include both real limitations of understanding the subject in its particulars (lack of empirical data or theoretical base) as well as human limitations in interpreting what is known (it was obvious for a long time that the sun circled the earth each 24 hours—the empirical evidence clearly supported this—those who challenged this obvious *perceived reality* were in considerable jeopardy). Different humans will develop different perceptions of reality, prompting the need for sophisticated message exchange concerning the problem.

Humans will organize their perceptions along different formats, even though they refer to the same reality. Each individual has some *basic referent system* (frame of reference; patterned approach to perceiving and transmitting a problem) which serves as an internalized heuristic for structuring personal interpretation of complex reality. (For example, if you were to request a statement from a sociologist, economist, geographer, political scientist, engineer, and urban planner concerning the problems of a major urban community, the structure of their response would vary considerably, both in emphasis and organizational mode: one reality, but many styles of perceiving and organizing abstractions of it.)

The result of this personal process of winnowing an impression of some complex idea into an organized and manageable scheme—a form capable of transmission—is a *conceptual map*. This is viewed as the internalized, organized, abstracted gestalt comprehension of complex reality that the author chooses to transmit or discuss. In some sense it is a model, analogous to the reality where actual concern rests. This conceptual map may or may not be committed to a formal written document.

Typically, this abstracted organized model of reality will appear as a professional paper (for gaming purposes the term *concept report* is adopted here). Because of the limitations of written communication the original reality will now appear in segmented form; each chapter or section will analyze a logical component as though it truly existed in isolation. Normally, special devices will be employed to emphasize the integrity of the reality; various graphics and/or statements indicating the linkage between components will be employed to suggest the actual dynamic. Consider the task of a research team which must present some radical new design for an internal combustion engine to the board of directors. The presentation is likely to be broken into presentations of the fuel system, the ignition system, the air intake and exhaust system, and so on. Contrast this approach to the team leader presenting a working model of the engine made of clear lucite (a simulation of the actual model) and responding to questions on its functional characteristics on demand from the board.

Having achieved an organized statement of complexity designed to serve as a starting point for discussion, we now encounter a mechanical problem. The report will be presented verbally to a group of potential respondents who may or may not have had prior access to the written statement. Upon completion of the presentation, discussion ensues. Respondents are selected in the order which they seek recognition, or more commonly, in the case where multiple respondents wish to speak, in some random pattern. To avoid chaos, conventions are employed which govern these "discussions." Respondents are discouraged or prohibited from private exchanges, and all voices must be recognized by the chair and a response given. Courtesy demands that the chair recognize those wishing to comment according to temporal equity, rather than according to the logical content of the proposed comment (the chair has no way to fathom who will address what aspect of the topic). Time constraints force limits to a given exchange to "allow time for other comments"; but, unfortunately, the other comment may prove to be more or less relevant. Potentially interesting "tangential" ideas must be stifled to insure a fair airing of the authors' views ("the chair regrets the necessity of moving on . . . certainly your speculation that the earth spins around the sun is very provocative, but we must stay with the central theme").

The result of this format is a less than perfect airing of the differing perception of complex reality, but nonetheless the technique does suffice in many instances and is in widespread usage.

MODEL NO. 4

This example is concerned with establishing communication about the same kinds of complexity as in the previous illustration. In this instance the communication mode is gaming/simulation. The process of perceiving, abstracting, and organizing the problem is much the same as the process employed in preparing for a lecture, but the device employed to facilitate communication about the topic is quite different (see Figure 15).

In this instance the basic abstraction (model) is stated in a concept report before being incorporated into the game itself, rather than in a verbalized model. The game construct becomes a logical, even if highly abstracted, analogue to the complex topic. The game designer makes his presentation through the game rather than through a verbal presentation or organized text. Participants are asked to identify with certain perspectives (roles) and are required to conform to certain logical constraints within that setting. Discussion of the system is prompted by the deliberate introduction of circumstances which tend to sharpen perception of dynamic relationships. A variety of events, problems, or issues can be articulated, and their introduction into the gaming context (pulse) helps to focus the many discussions simultaneously underway. The individual discussions are as in Model No. 2, except these are many parallel discussions underway at a given moment. The discussions obtain their focus both from the basic model represented in the game and from the pulse, which is also a device for organizing the progress of the discussion. Because the pulse may be either prespecified or introduced as a result of participant need during

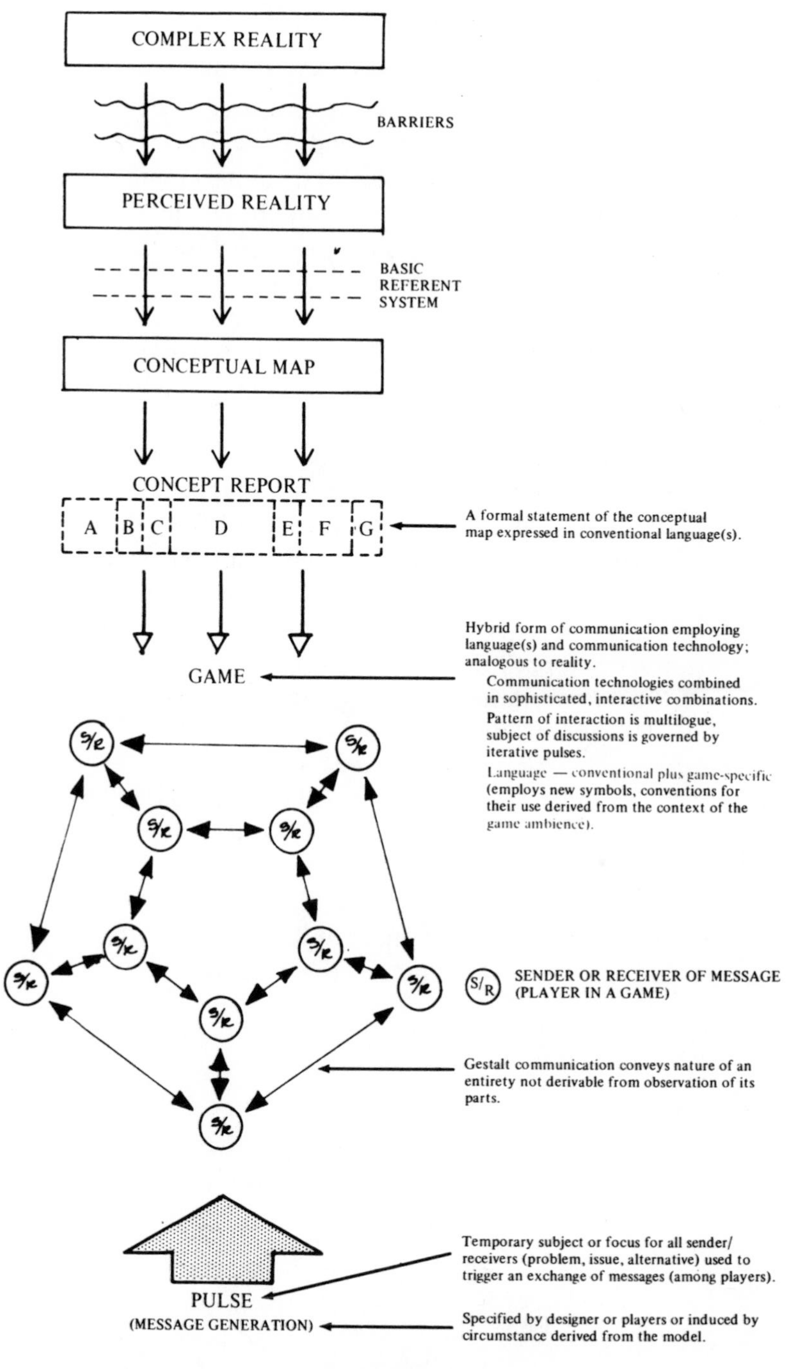
COMPLEX REALITY
BARRIERS
PERCEIVED REALITY
BASIC
REFERENT
SYSTEM
CONCEPTUAL MAP
CONCEPT REPORT
A
B
C
D
E
F
G
A formal statement of the conceptual map expressed in conventional language(s).
GAME
Hybrid form of communication employing language(s) and communication technology; analogous to reality.
Communication technologies combined in sophisticated, interactive combinations.
Pattern of interaction is multilogue, subject of discussions is governed by iterative pulses.
Language — conventional plus game-specific (employs new symbols, conventions for their use derived from the context of the game ambience).
S/R
SENDER OR RECEIVER OF MESSAGE (PLAYER IN A GAME)
Gestalt communication conveys nature of an entirety not derivable from observation of its parts.
Temporary subject or focus for all sender/receivers (problem, issue, alternative) used to trigger an exchange of messages (among players).
PULSE
(MESSAGE GENERATION)
Specified by designer or players or induced by circumstance derived from the model.

FIGURE 15.
Model No. 4: Future's Language
Communicating Through Gaming Simulation

play, there is considerable latitude both in setting the agenda for discussion as well as in establishing the sequence of deliberation. This permits some escape from the rigid sequentiality of the formal lecture, which must go logically from beginning to end. The game construct is all of one piece, and has no logical entry or exit point per se. This permits the individual to enter into the multilogue from his own frame of reference or point of perspective. It permits and encourages a tumbling ongoing discussion among changing and unstable coalitions who come together as their ideas coincide, and as quickly break away to form new conversational units. (All of those back of the room whispered sessions that the chairman has to continuously squelch are encouraged to form and pursue their productive course.)

Because the respondent is roaming freely within a logical construct he discerns its shape and characteristics by a series of vignettes of his own making. He is free to explore in a sequence which appears logical to him, rather than be constrained to an arbitrary and preordained path of inquiry. In reviewing this model it is important to differentiate between multilogue and many dialogues being conducted simultaneously. Multilogue is the organized simultaneous inquiry into some complex topic; contrast this with a cocktail party which is characterized by many simultaneous dialogues covering a broad array of disjointed subject matter.

The next chapter presents a further elaboration of gaming as a communication form, including a model which attempts to present the dynamics of the process.

4 GAMING AS A FUTURE'S LANGUAGE

The first chapter addressed the need for gestalt, or holistic, communication. The arguments presented there are summarized in this quote from Rhyne (1973):

> The interweaving of problems in this era has forced attention to wider and more complex fields by each decision maker and by staff or research efforts set to aid him. The mode of understanding that is needed is one of gestalt appreciation rather than explicit knowledge of bits of data. This is true whether one views the current Macroproblem as a citizen, a responsible executive agent in government or business, or a researcher. The extent of the field to be appreciated and the contraction of the time available for doing so interdicts the normal, experiential way of gaining deep appreciation, so vicarious routes are needed. (p. 96)

As described previously in this section, a variety of devices are employed in the various modes of communication to reduce their inherent sequentiality, to improve their ability to convey gestalt. The continuum (Figure 4) used the term "Future's Language" for those listed at the right-hand extreme.

This usage is meant to imply that these forms will prove of greatest value in those circumstances where the need to convey gestalt is urgent. It is not being suggested that they are the "language of the future"; nor is it suggested that Future's Language is limited to gaming/simulation. Other examples exist and more are sure to be devised. What *is* suggested is that gaming/simulation, properly conceived and employed, is a powerful tool both for conveying gestalt and for explaining alternative situations that could not otherwise be managed.

There is, however, a problem, an impediment to the use of gaming. Quoting Rhyne:

> Intuition and gestalt appreciations now are in disrepute, both in government and among professional users of intelligence to solve problems. (p. 99)

> In the intellectual climate of the times, intuition and supra-logical insight tend to be classed with alchemy and magic; efforts to invent an alternative to prosaic exposition will have to be justified to skeptics before first trials will be permitted. With all of these urgencies and obstacles, there still are signs that spectacular success may lie just beyond the first serious trials. (p. 93)

Certainly many of the ill-conceived uses of gaming/simulation to date have not helped—the technique has not been well understood and enthusiastic proponents have used it beyond its capability. Gaming is not a predictive device, not a panacea to be plugged into the problem of the moment. It can be usefully employed for gaining perspective on complex circumstance; it is particularly useful for guiding speculation about future circumstances.

SOME EXAMPLES OF FUTURE'S LANGUAGES

There are a variety of communication modes which fall into the category of Future's Language, some of which are described below:

1. Cartography

The central objective of the common highway map is to convey an overview of a particular geographic area (city, state or region). The user does not "read" a map in a sequential fashion, rather the map is used as a framework for problem solving (for example, How do I get from place "X" to place "Y"?). Cartographers use a special language; the symbols employed for a given type of mapping are unique and explicit rules are used when employing them.

Each map is of course distinct; it addresses a specific problem (a particular geographic area for a precise purpose). As a consequence there are available a wide array of maps for any given city, of differing scale, technique, and level of detail (routing of public transportation, house numbering, highway map, land use and zoning maps, district maps for a wide variety of municipal purposes, and so on). Maps show explicit linkages in two dimensional geographical terms, and, therefore, permit the user to explore alternative routes between nodes at the discretion of the individual. Contrast this with prose, which must be read sequentially from beginning to end; a map has no beginning or end—one starts from any point that makes sense! Maps have a basic universality in that they are prepared for a broad range of groups, sophisticated or not, as the problem situation may require.

In terms of time frame, most maps purport to illustrate present time; however, most are outdated at the time of their printing. They are frequently used to illustrate speculative future conditions (for example, a proposed real estate development), or some historical circumstance. The mapping technique does not lend itself to ready alteration; however, the user can make minor modifications. Unfortunately, maps are inherently static and although they convey a gestalt of a given moment in time, they are of marginal value in conveying a sense of change. To overcome this limitation they are sometimes employed sequentially, with progressive maps indicating the same subject at different points in time.

2. Animated Cartography

This technique permits the conveyance of gestalt in both geographic and temporal dimensions. A sequence of maps is prepared, photographed as still "frames," and bled together using a time-lapse technique. The resultant product lets the viewer see the emergence of an historical pattern (or a future state) in a dynamic gestalt mode.

3. Iconic Models

Some three-dimensional examples of Future's Language exist in the form of iconic models. An architectural model of a proposed building qualifies as a Future's Language. It is holistic—at least within the limited perspective of the area represented. Detail may be presented at varying degrees from crude illustrations of the rough proportions of shapes and spaces to exquisite detail.

While such three-dimensional models are typically viewed as a gestalt, it is equally true that the primary purpose of such models is to respond to "what if" questions that might be posed by an interested observer. Questions pertaining to architectural detail, the functional relationship between buildings, and pedestrian or vehicular circulation are specific inquiries which are "pulsed" through the model by the designer and/or client. The response inevitably introduces the questioner to aspects beyond that of the specific inquiry.

Such physical models are easily understood by people without technical expertise. They are particularly useful when dealing with an audience of diverse sophistication and jargon because they visually mimic a world that the observers all know from their own perspective. Such models can represent any point in time, and are frequently representations of past events or future possibilities. In their design phase, at least, they are quite transient. That is, it is common for a design team working with crude architectural models to change the construction again and again as their perceptions change. Such models inevitably depict a particular problem situation. As with the previous examples drawn from cartography, physical models may be used to illustrate dynamic circumstance by having, for instance, replaceable components (multiple facades showing alternative design treatments). One researcher has developed a computer program which presents its results on a video screen. The user can gain an impression of the aesthetics of a proposed shopping center by "walking" through the area. As the structures are modified, the impression changes. As with a map, the viewer enters from whatever point he wishes.

4. Flow Charts

The analysis of any complex system requires the simultaneous analysis of many variables. For example, in order to represent the transportation system of a community, many more dimensions must be considered than those represented on a two-dimensional map: the economics of one mode of transportation relative to a second; traveling habits of the citizens currently using the system; the possible changes in the clientele likely to use the system at future points in time; the concept of time-distance as it is influenced by the system itself; the degree of possible subsidization of the system; the existing land use pattern generating demand for the migrations of people; potential changes in the land use system which might alter the demand for transport; and so on. The analysis of complex systems such as transportation has required the introduction of increasingly sophisticated simulation techniques. But simulation must be preceded by "flow charting." The completed flow chart becomes the "blueprint" for the construction of the actual simulation. Flow charting represents a graphic presentation of the various elements of the system, with linear pointers going from box to box to illustrate flows, linkages, and impacts.

The purpose of a flow chart is to convey the imagery of an entire system. It is not uncommon to see flow charts broken into several levels: a preliminary chart shows the major systems; a secondary chart shows the major components of a second level of the system; and at another level, very detailed flow charts are prepared to show the specific linkages of the system. In this case one proceeds progressively through the series of images of the system. This illustrates the specification of detail at an appropriate level.

Flow charts are presented as though they were sequential; or more properly, as though the system that they represent were sequential. This is a major limitation of the technique since the processes are usually of a more gestalt character. Nonetheless, the flow charting is designed to permit the pulsing of the logic of a particular situation through the flow charted structure so that one can follow in one's mind the path of logic that is expected to occur. In this process, of course, linkages become explicit to the extent that they are represented in the flow chart. Unfortunately, the technique is elitest; that is, it is best understood by a sophisticated audience. Nonetheless, examples do exist of simple flow charts being put to use by lay audiences.

Generally, flow charts are used to represent a system that is being conjectured as a future possibility, although they could represent any appropriate time frame. In their formation they are extremely transient, and the designers of a system will change and rechange the flow chart in the process of arguing about the character of the system. As with the previous examples of cartographic maps and iconic models, flow charting is also situation specific in terms of its content; however, it illustrates more graphically the possibility of the concept of a "frame" language. That is, within the relatively simple and straightforward system of flow charting, one may substitute a variety of subject matter with ease.

5. War Rooms

War or situation rooms are another useful example of a gestalt communication mode. These usually contain a cartographic map and/or physical model of the region of concern, but there are additional supporting systems which provide other information. Usually the physical representation (map and/or model) is kept current, and this updating makes it a dynamic process. Various accounting systems and/or simulations (which may or may not be computerized) provide data on historic, current or projected future conditions. These rooms are a careful abstraction of the most significant real-world characteristics. They provide an overview in both a temporal and geographic context, but more importantly numerous additional dimensions are integrated into the gestalt.

6. Gaming/Simulation

Gaming/simulation goes one step further than the war room example. In addition to the materials described above, the gaming/simulation will have a series of scenarios depicting possible courses of action. Various decisionmakers will be represented by humans acting out significant roles. By acting out "what if" situations, alternative futures can be explored.

CHARACTERISTICS OF FUTURE'S LANGUAGES

Earlier, in Chapter 2, the various modes of communication were arrayed along a continuum and their central characteristics analyzed (see Figure 9). The six criteria used in that example are now used to explore the nature of Future's Languages, with particular emphasis on interpreting their significance to gaming/simulation. Some individual games are used here to illustrate the characteristics; those familiar with other games may select examples for mental reference.

Sequential/Gestalt Constraint

This requires the use of some device created for each specific Future's Language to assist in establishing and retaining an imagery of the "big picture"—the total scheme under consideration. Such devices are often graphic (drawings, diagrams, schematics) and frequently will be three-dimensional (perspective drawings, architect's models), but may be supplemented by sophisticated computer simulations which, upon proper inquiry, will reveal the dimensions of the system. The introduction of role playing and the use of scenario are still other devices employed to assist in conveying gestalt.

The primary purpose of any game is to convey gestalt; to be successful it must convey an overall perspective of the problem at hand. Virtually all games have been prompted into existence to meet this requirement. Although many different devices are employed by game designers to obtain this objective (visual devices such as boards or graphs, flow charts, pie charts, and the like), it is during actual play that the ultimate success of the design can be perceived. Direct observation of game players will quickly reveal the ability of the game to convey gestalt. Success is marked by good communication both inter- and intra-team, as well as by the quality of the discussions which ensue during the critique. Although players identify with only one role, it is from this perspective that they gain a perception of the total system conveyed by the game. A well known example is the *Cornell Land Use Game (CLUG)* which uses a gridded board with blocks of wood representing buildings. Players are confronted with the problem of designing the growth of the city to meet whatever specifications they may establish. The game could, theoretically, be played without this board; it is not, however, a practical possibility.

Universality/Specificity

All Future's Languages are problem-specific and as such must be designed to meet the need of a particular client group. As a consequence, the range of sophistication and, therefore, the methodology employed will be enormously diverse. Fortunately many Future's Languages lend themselves to basic structures, or frames, which can be employed repeatedly in different situations through the device of altering the content. (The rules of flow charting are consistent but the content will vary in each application.) All games are problem-specific; that is, they address a particular situation and in any given event or play of that game the subject matter is explicit and unique.

Unfortunately, many games have been used inappropriately, out of their intended context. One response to this problem has been the invention of frame games which are specifically designed for a fresh loading of content for each application.

Spontaneity

Because they are used to facilitate discussion about complex subject matter, the various Future's Languages tend to be somewhat complicated in construction. When completed and operationalized, their ease of use varies considerably among the many different modes. Gaming/simulation, properly employed, is inherently spontaneous. Participants who overcome the early difficulties associated with "start-up" procedures become deeply enmeshed in the technique.

Mutability

This characteristic relates to the ability of the mode to be transformed while in use. Future's Languages are basically transient in format to permit the restructuring or more careful articulation of the problem as viewed by those participating in the dialogue. Future's Languages are a dynamic communication form; they must respond during use to changing perceptions of the problem.

Well-designed games are quite transient in character. They permit the restructuring or redefinition of the game itself during the event of play. Evidence of this can be obtained by taking any given game and running it with different audiences. The more thoughtful games deliberately structure mechanisms which encourage and facilitate player or operator modification during the event of play. The present range of games varies tremendously in format. Some are quite rigid and must be played according to the rules. However, there has been a tendency for some time for games to become increasing flexible in actual use; virtually all of them are modified by the operator to suit the conditions of the run, or in response to player needs.

Range

Among Future's Languages there is a strong need for a catholicity of design. They can be designed to accommodate groups employing a specific jargon, and those which have an inherent diversity of jargon and/or markedly different levels of sophistication.

Games have a basic catholicity of design. There is hardly an audience for which a game has not been designed: high school students, university use, business leaders, community groups, military strategists, diplomats, and so on. This is best illustrated by the incredible profusion of examples currently on the market. Some require nothing more than a sheet of paper or a blackboard and can be completed by a wide array of participants in a short time. Other games, designed to meet more sophisticated audiences, are used for training and in actual decisionmaking contexts.

Message Characteristics

Future's Languages have an ability to present a future orientation. This means the representation of any time frame other than the present (including the past, future, or any alternative to a present situation). Their purpose is to explore alternatives, to develop a sophisticated mental response to "what if" questions, and to permit the formulation of analogy for exploration of alternatives where no prior basis for analogy exists.

Most games have a setting other than a real and current time frame. Generally, they explore some immediate future, although some deal with past circumstances or alternatives to the present reality. Future's Languages are able to achieve the transmission of gestalt imagery in differing time perspectives because of three inherent qualities.

Pulsing of Alternatives

Future's Languages permit the pulsing of specific, tangible inquiries or alternatives to permit the correlation with a holistic image. There is a correlation here with the strict sequentiality of traditional communication forms. Both spoken and written language, even in their sophisticated forms, advance through a strict sequentiality (sentence follows sentence, thought follows thought). The sequential pulsing of inquiries through a Future's Language is more sophisticated in that a pulse in itself becomes a logical and coherent proposition, independently formed, evaluated, and comprehended. As such, it provides the focus of inquiry as it is tested against the gestalt or holistic image provided.

Common to all games is a pulsing of thought or inquiry. This takes several forms, the most common of which is rounds in which players sequentially make their decisions. Games are almost invariably cyclical, and each cycle permits iterative questions that must be resolved in the total context of the game. The common use of issues, problems, or an iterative decision set in games illustrates this point. This process is frequently modified by the inclusion of events that are either preprogrammed or triggered by circumstance that develops, or random events which focus the players' attention on some new problem or aspect of the situation at hand. For example, in *CLUG* every fifth year a special event takes into account the possibility of random disaster.

Specification of Detail

A Future's Language provides the participants with the opportunity to approach the topic from any perspective which is relevant to that participant; inquiry is permitted at the level of abstraction that seems appropriate to the respondent. The context or format of the Future's Language makes the logical correlation of these idiosyncratic inquiries to the gestalt convenient, if not inherent.

Games permit the specification of detail at an appropriate level within the context of the holistic image. A central issue in the design and construction of a game is proper determination of the *level of abstraction.* There are now several dozen "urban" games in existence. These range from relatively simple role playing exercises which emphasize power structure and human interaction to gaming simulations with a computer component that accurately conveys very detailed characteristics of some subsystem—for example, the housing market. Some games are actually nested, games within games, in order to handle detail at increasingly more precise levels. Still others, for example some frame games, allow the participants to specify the level of detail themselves.

Explication of Linkages

Future's Languages have the ability to display, make explicit, or permit the recording of linkages between major segments of the holistic imagery; they create an awareness of feedback. As a formulated inquiry is pulsed through the Future's Language, the participants obtain, through both direct and serendipitous means, an awareness of the complexity being explored.

Games are particularly valuable for making the linkages between the major components of the system being represented explicit. These linkages are discovered during the play of the game, and they should be emphasized during the critique process. The pursuit of the logic relevant to a given issue by a given player leads to confrontation with parallel but separate tracks initiated by other players working from different perspectives. The results of this interaction lead in serendipitous fashion to increased understanding of the total reality by each player. In *CLUG* the correlation between the interests of competing teams, the transportation system and its costs, utilities and their costs, the assessment of property for tax purposes, and similar variables become self-evident to the player and have a high correlation with real-world phenomena.

These basic characteristics, common to all Future's Languages, help to explain the effectiveness of games in such a broad diversity of applications. This discussion does not mean to suggest that gaming/simulation has preempted as *the* Future's Language. However, if certain rules, concepts, or principles are employed consistently, a game product can certainly qualify in a wide variety of situations.

COMMUNICATING THROUGH GAMING

For our purposes, *gaming/simulation* is defined as a gestalt communication mode, a Future's Language which combines a game-specific language and appropriate communication technologies with the multilogue interaction pattern. This combination of components is unique among the various communication modes—especially when one considers that it is presented to the participants in an interactive mode (as contrasted with the uni-directional pattern of film or television).

Earlier, gaming/simulation was presented as being at the extreme right margin of the communication continuum. The characteristics of this form and their derivation from the unique combination of components is shown in Figure 16. The unusually high ability of gaming/simulation to provide a holistic imagery is its central characteristic.

Gestalt communication differs significantly from sequential communication in that it implies a less rigid transmission of ideas and emphasizes a heuristic understanding of some complex reality. This permits the receiver a greater flexibility in addressing facets of complexity than could be obtained from a sequential presentation. A sequential presentation is burdensome and exhausting; but more importantly, complex reality is a system which can never be comprehended by the exclusive examination of the individual components.

Chapter 3 presented four models of human communication. A fifth model, presented here (see Figure 17) attempts to show the dynamics of the communication process in the gaming mode. Complex reality is represented in the diagram as a hexagon, with the various nodes representing decision points, and all lines connecting these points representing potential information flows. It would be preferable to visualize a dodecahedron rather than a plane, since the typical problem will be multifaceted. In theory, there is a possibility of a message exchange between any given decision unit and all others. In practice, some of these message linkages will be mandatory, others optional, and still others nonexistent or insignificant.

In Figure 17 the game itself is explored in greater depth. Several items of significance must be emphasized. First,

CHARACTERISTIC	NATURE OF GAMING/SIMULATION	DERIVES FROM THESE COMPONENTS OF THIS COMMUNICATION MODE
SEQUENTIAL/ GESTALT	Highest ability to convey gestalt of the various modes of communication	Multilogue Interactive use of communications technology game-specific language
UNIVERSALITY/ SPECIFICITY	Highly problem or situation specific, low versatility for any *given* game	Game-specific language
SPONTANEITY	Game construction requires great effort but use is spontaneous	Game-specific language Multilogue
MUTABILITY	During each use of a game a distinct jargon will emerge.	Game-specific language
RANGE (CATHOLICITY)	Games can be designed for use with a wide variety of clients.	Game-specific language (number of supersymbols, level of abstraction)
MESSAGE CHARACTERISTICS	Conveys gestalt of complex reality as well as specification of various details.	Multilogue

FIGURE 16.
Characteristics of Gaming/Simulation

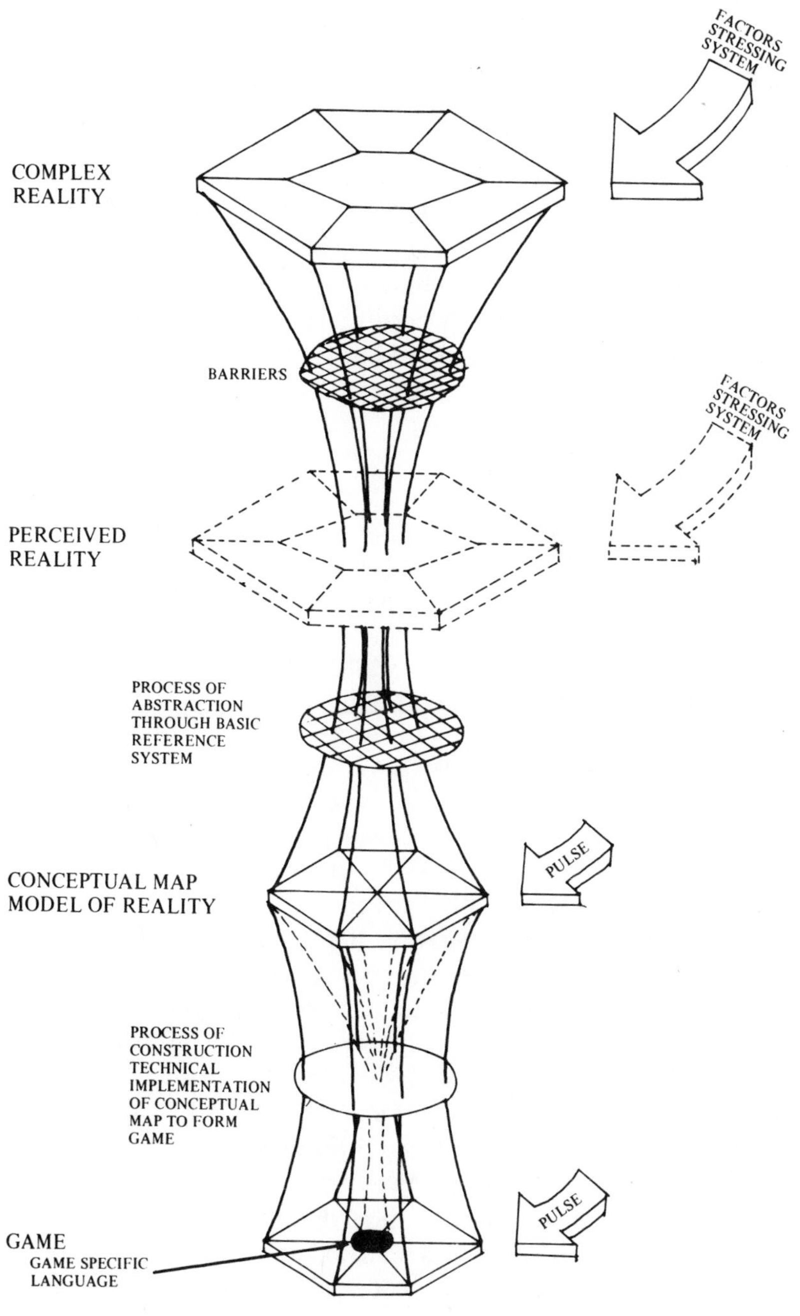

FIGURE 17.
A Model of Communication Through Gaming/Simulation

the players are assumed to be engaged in different roles requiring differing perceptions of the reality modeled by the game. Because they are simultaneously engaged in the process, the message interchange pattern contains many concurrent dimensions and the term dialogue is insufficient to describe the process. Rather, it should be thought of as many parallel and simultaneous dialogues (multilogue), all pertaining to some aspect of a complex phenomenon. Serendipitous occurrence, both during the play of the game and in the organized critique which follows, will heighten the significance of these message exchanges in terms of what they convey to the player about the nature of the complex reality.

Whatever reality may be, there are always barriers to its perception; and the perceived reality which filters through those barriers becomes the basis for discussion. Because of the complexity involved, both abstraction and organization are required, and our internalized heuristics guide us in formulating a model of reality. This internalized model or conceptual map, whether or not independently committed to paper, becomes the basis for the construction of the game. If the process is successful, the game is in some sense analogous to reality. The process of converting the mental imagery to an operational game is achieved through a process of construction (see Section III for a detailed description of this process).

This process of abstraction entails both the complex problem under consideration and the factors which are brought to bear on the system. These are independently analyzed, abstracted, and organized for later systematic introduction into the game. They are called pulses and their existence allows the participants to gain insight into the abstracted system. That is, the participants explore reality through the consideration of iterative pulses of information which focus them in their different perspectives on a common or shared problem, issue, or alternative. The pulse, then, becomes an organizational device, somewhat analogous to the organization of sentence structure, which encourages multilogue to be focused on a shared phenomenon, even though many such dialogues may be simultaneously underway. It is this phenomenon that permits the serendipitous discovery of the nature of complexity.

It is important to note that these pulses of information may be either designer induced and/or player induced, and they may be predetermined, random, or triggered by certain events or occurrences in the play of the game.

A research team engaged in simulating any complex phenomena may succeed in sharing a perception of reality. If the team is interdisciplinary, the basic referent systems of the individual members will produce individual conceptual maps of that reality and the specialists will literally talk past each other in the dialogue. A consistent effort by an interdisciplinary team will result in the development of a special modification of conventional language; their mutual exchanges would be incomprehensible to a new arrival. These professionals develop a shared jargon, with tacit agreement on its proper use. This facilitates their attempts at developing a simulation which, in the final analysis, must be a melding of their individual perceptions. Couldn't this process be systematically undertaken in anticipation of some research task? This would speed the process of research and increase the efficiency of the team. It would also provide a device by which a new participant could share the perceptions of the initial group.

Gaming/simulation will employ a game-specific language. It may be deliberately designed into the game structure or acquired inadvertently by the players as a jargon to assist in this multilogue. The game-specific language is a critical element in the gaming process; it implies the thoughtful invention of jargon as part of game design. It must be sufficiently complex to improve discussion about a specific problem, but simple enough to be learned during the normal course of play.

It is specifically suggested that the game model, when functioning during the event of a game, is the basis for a game-specific language. The jargon employed to describe roles or components of reality which are modeled becomes the *supersymbols* (symbols which are unique to the game), while the basic game structure or model, including the constraints of message potential between decision units as well as the behavior of individual decision units in response to the message, becomes the set of conventions governing the use of the game-specific symbols. These two, in conjunction, constitute the game-specific language.

In an early diagram (Figure 6), Grand-père informed us how he had survived without the past anterior verb form for 87 years. More correctly, he had survived this period without labelling or intellectualizing the form. It is quite probable that he used it nonetheless. Grand-père learned his grammar in an operational context; similarly, the ambience of the game provides the context for learning, in an operational sense, the meaning of the special symbols employed to represent the abstracted reality.

Communication through a gaming model entails not only multilogue among the players, but also communication between players and designer (see Figure 18). The game is iterative, involving cycles of play each of which mimics some real-world time phase but which varies in focus depending on the pulse of information used to trigger multilogue. Discussion is followed by decision, and decision by processing. These results must be reviewed; during the *critique* players must be encouraged to focus on the reality which the game model attempts to represent. If there are *challenges* by the players, these must be resolved by offering evidence to sustain the model, or through the modification of the model to more accurately reflect the new understanding of reality.

SOME THOUGHTS ON LEARNING THROUGH GAMING

The early literature in gaming emphasizes a perspective on gaming as an environment for learning. More recent work of a theoretical nature suggests that game designers have been on the right track. Moore and Anderson (1969) have been involved in the articulation of basic principles underlying the design of good educational environments for some time. In a recent article they state four underlying principles (1969: 585):

(1) Perspectives principle—A given environment is more productive if it permits and facilitates the taking of more perspectives towards the problem than another environment.

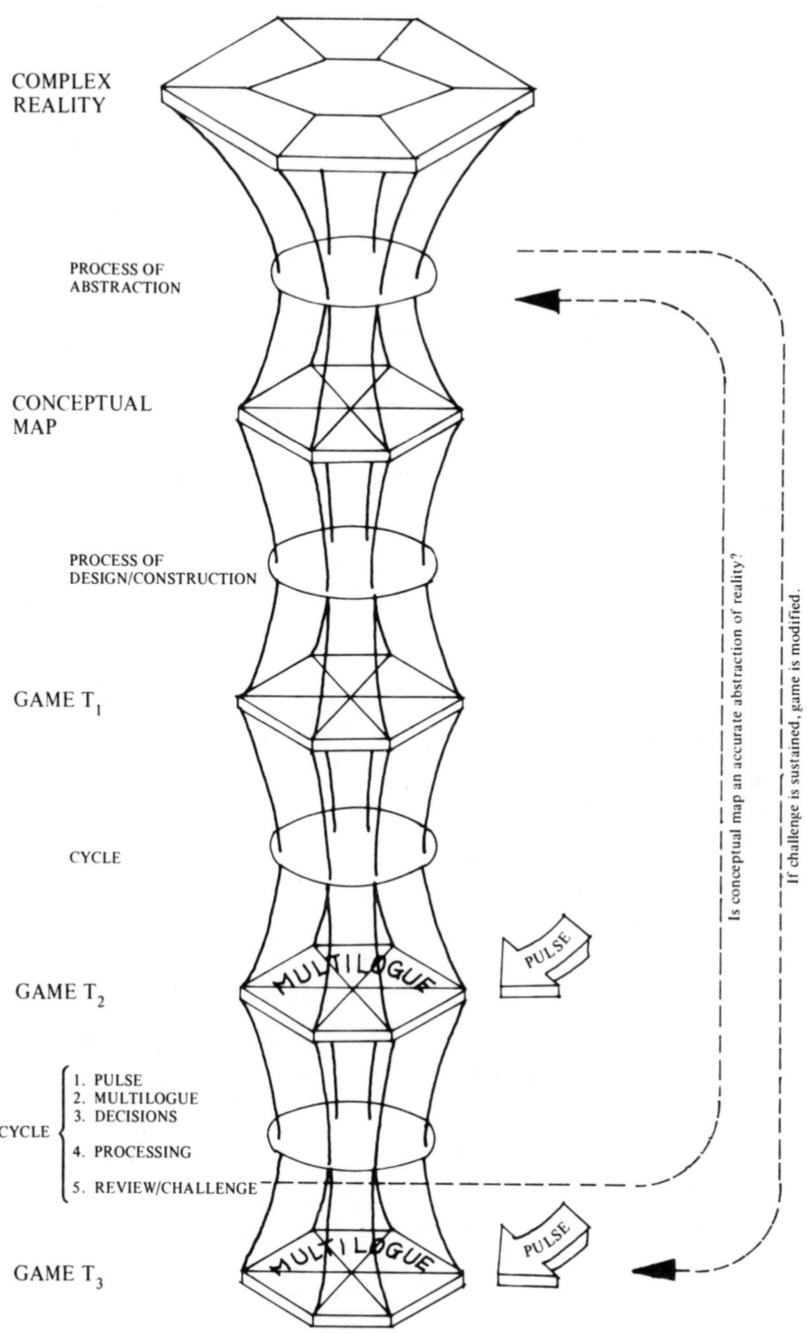

FIGURE 18.
Challenging the Game Model

(2) Autotelic principle—The environment must be safe for experimentation of even the most outrageous or improbable sort without high personal risk.

(3) Productive principle—This implies the ability of the learner to deduce or make probable inference within the context of the educational environment. This requires an environment which is logically and coherently structured, permitting the learner to make leaps of faith to some other perspective or level of thought.

(4) Personalization principle—That environment is most productive which permits the greatest responsiveness to the learner's activities; it is an environment that encourages the learner first to find a question and then find an answer.

Most existing games appear to have been constructed with the concept of an "environment for learning" as an underlying rationale. The rigidity of some of the early models and applications has given way to more flexible, more transient vehicles. Examination of a broad range of games suggests that they do apply the four principles suggested by Moore and Anderson, whether through intuition or deliberate design.

The "environment for learning" concept can be stated differently. The learner is more receptive to information if it is in response to a felt need and if it is presented in a context understood or perceived by the learner. The fragmentation of knowledge, which is best illustrated by the broad array of individual courses offered by learning institutions, is a fairly recent phenomenon. The formidable increase in knowledge has necessitated this fragmentation, but man as a learner stems from a heritage where knowledge was of a piece and new information was incrementally accrued in a real-world context. In simpler times man had a totality of perspective that was part of the fabric of life. As he advanced through life, he encountered in more or less iterative fashion the same pattern supplemented by modification and change brought by the course of time.

Great-grandfather knew the entire process for building his house: what materials to use and how to put them together. But his great-grandson would hardly think of starting to build a house without a blueprint. A blueprint, mental or physical, serves several functions. It stores all the information for building the house until it is needed. It can be used as a common set of reference points when great-grandson wants to discuss matters with a contractor. And it organizes a myriad of details into a compact consistent whole so the information can be seen simultaneously; the relationships between bits of data are clear, and the information can be easily retrieved.

In gaming/simulation the "conceptual map" serves as a mental blueprint to help convey complex systems. The conceptual map classifies, sorts, and stores information; it provides a heuristic language to be used as a common symbol structure for discussing a given complex system. Data conveyed through a conceptual map ceases to be mere bits of information; rather it becomes heuristic wisdom. However, a conceptual map is not assimilated as a static structure or by static means; it is built up iteratively over time.

Learning or comprehension can be viewed as a circular process, or more properly, a spiral. Each concentric movement of 360° represents the logical acquisition of knowledge about a new topic, characterized by completeness at a given level of detail; the distance between the spiral rings represents elapsed time. The completion of a spiral ring implies a certain integrity or perspective to the knowledge acquired. It provides the context (reference point) for the next ring. To the extent that the gestalt is incomplete, comprehension and retention of further detail will be inhibited. The relevance of this "spiral" to a discussion about complex systems is two-fold: (1) it points out the necessity for establishing context before learning can take place, and (2) it describes a learning process which synthesizes increasing detail into overviews or iterative gestalts.

Gaming can be viewed as fitting this spiral concept since games proceed by permitting players to build up a more complete conceptual map during successive rounds of play. Games iterate in both a major and minor sequence. The minor cycle takes the players through one entire iteration of the game environment. The major sequence starts with a series of cycles which introduce the player to the context of the game itself;

followed by a second group of cycles in which the player is encouraged to learn new material through the experience of several further iterations; followed by the final stage in which a critique is used to draw together the experiences which have been encountered in some deliberate and organized way. Players go through basically three stages of perception of the game environment:

(1) Initially, the player is put off by the complexity and by the array of information being presented.
(2) The player enters into a stage where he is in control of, or at least at ease with, the environment and during this time will explore with ingenuity a variety of options that come to mind within the context of the game.
(3) The player develops a sophistication which exceeds the limits of the game and withdraws voluntarily from further participation.

These observations explain the notion of a learning spiral. The early iterations establish a basis of understanding or gestalt which serve as reference in the subsequent cycles. As play continues and more complexity is introduced, the player from his own perspective and in his own time perceives problems, asks questions, and finds answers within the context of the game. As learning progresses the player recognizes that the game as an abstraction can only mimic the world or reality being gamed, and turns his attention to the actual reality. At this point a critique is particularly effective because the participants of the game event share a "language" or jargon derived from the game event and this can be useful to them in exploring reality.

We learn through games, then, because if they are properly designed they represent abstract symbolic maps of multidimensional phenomena which serve as basic reference systems for tucking away the bits and pieces of detail that are transmitted. In particular, they assist in the formulation of inquiry from a variety of obtuse angles or perspectives, which are meaningful to the individual making the inquiry and which can only be transmitted through an N-dimensional, abstract, symbolic-mapping procedure. If the previous observations on the character of change in the world since World War II are valid, they could perhaps be summarized as follows. Before World War II the need for pragmatic information and fact, learned by rote, was imperative. In the new era, there is an urgent need for the acquisition of heuristics—a flexible set of highly abstract conceptual tools which will let the participant view new and emerging situations, having no precedent, in a way that permits comprehension.

The management of resources, natural and human, is like a fourth-dimensional problem we three-dimensional beings cannot comprehend. We are unable personally to encounter the reality, and therefore unable to communicate with one another, even at elite levels, about possible management schemes. We desperately need to relax the constraints on our communication. This means moving to the gestalt end of the communications continuum. Here, through the proper use of gaming/simulation we find very strong promise for reestablishing the comprehension of totality which is necessary for the intelligent management of any complex system.

SECTION III

INTRODUCTION TO SECTION III

Section II established the rationale for viewing gaming as a new communication form. If this perspective is acceptable as a premise, it becomes necessary to formalize the conventions currently in use and to identify new areas where the specification of convention might be productive. This section examines gaming technique and practice with this objective in mind.

One caution is required. Gaming/simulation is one of the most costly modes of communication for both construction and use. It is incumbent upon the potential user to consider alternative modes carefully. Before proceeding with the gaming technique, every effort should be made to ascertain that the client's need cannot be met by some less cumbersome mode.

This section includes four chapters: "The Game Design Process," "Game Components," "Repertoire of Techniques" employed in gaming, and "Interpretive Criteria."

The game design process presented in Chapter 5 considers three major areas: design, the deliberate process of expressing an idea set through gaming; construction, the mechanical phase of assembly and testing; and use, the actual employment of the game product with all its attendant documentation, training, dissemination, and modification. In the abstract the game design process is viewed as sequential; the game designer proceeds logically from point to point. In practice, the designer will attempt a simultaneous solution and will move from sector to sector in any convenient order. Nonetheless, the presentation in Chapter 5 views the process as though it were more rigidly sequential. The appendices offer two supplements to this chapter. Appendix A, "Specifications for Game Design," is a pragmatic list of questions that the game user or designer should answer before beginning construction of a game. Appendix B, "Conceptual Mapping," suggests a series of procedures which might be useful in the process of developing the conceptual map. This addition is offered because of the strongly held belief that most gaming efforts would benefit from an explicit presentation of the model which the game attempts to convey.

Chapter 6 defines game components in terms of the *symbolic structure* employed, the use of *scenario,* and processing *procedures* including both *rules* and mechanics. This presentation might be viewed as a rudimentary effort toward a "manual of style" or basic "grammar" of gaming/simulation. As such it tries to do no more than capture the main aspects of current usage. It is not intended as prescriptive, except as shared conventions might ease communication problems among gamers and facilitate more useful game products.

One major difficulty facing the game operator is ready access to a complete library of game products and/or conventional search procedures for exploring a game once in hand. Chapter 7 reviews the repertoire of techniques employed by the gaming profession in terms of basic styles or referent systems employed—techniques employed to improve learning through gaming; techniques to ensure a smooth running game; and a variety of elements which contribute to *gaminess.* These materials are intended as a general reference system through which existing games might be interpreted. These ideas might be useful to the neophyte in organizing a perspective from which generalized conclusions about the content, character and possible utility of a game can be obtained.

Finally, in Chapter 8, *interpretive criteria* are developed. These are presented as the minimum information set required of the game designer about a product being made available to the public. These criteria take the form of a set of questions which must be answered in writing by the game designer as a guide for the potential user. The designer is expected to specify basic information about the circumstances which induced the game, the availability of the game kit, the character of the expected participants, the type of player involvement and the time required, the steps of play and plot outline, the main dynamic of play, and finally some assistance to the user in evaluating the product.

Throughout Chapters 5 to 8 certain tentative ideas have been identified and set off in italics in the text. While these appear to be valid, they remain hypothetical. They have been given special attention in the hope that over a period of time they can be verified, modified, replaced, or rejected as invalid.

5 THE GAME DESIGN PROCESS

Game design is a combination of mimicry of existing game formats and styles, an elusive but real "art," and certain design principles, some reasonably well articulated and some just beginning to emerge. At the present stage of development in the field of gaming, most, if not all, games represent a "happening" rather than the product of a deliberate design process (see Figure 19). One prominent designer insists that his games convey no "message"; rather, he contends, they are free and ethereal situations which the participant can direct from "inside" the game. To establish this as basically spurious reasoning substitute "book" for game. The function of a book may well be to establish creative or innovative thought by the reader, thought which may go well beyond the specific content of the book. Nonetheless, the author of the book must intend some message or purpose (for example, to inspire creative thought) before a coherent book can be assembled. Similarly, the author of a game must have an express and coherent purpose or "message" to guide the construction of a game. Only the clear articulation of this purpose permits the rational selection of gaming as the appropriate communication mode.

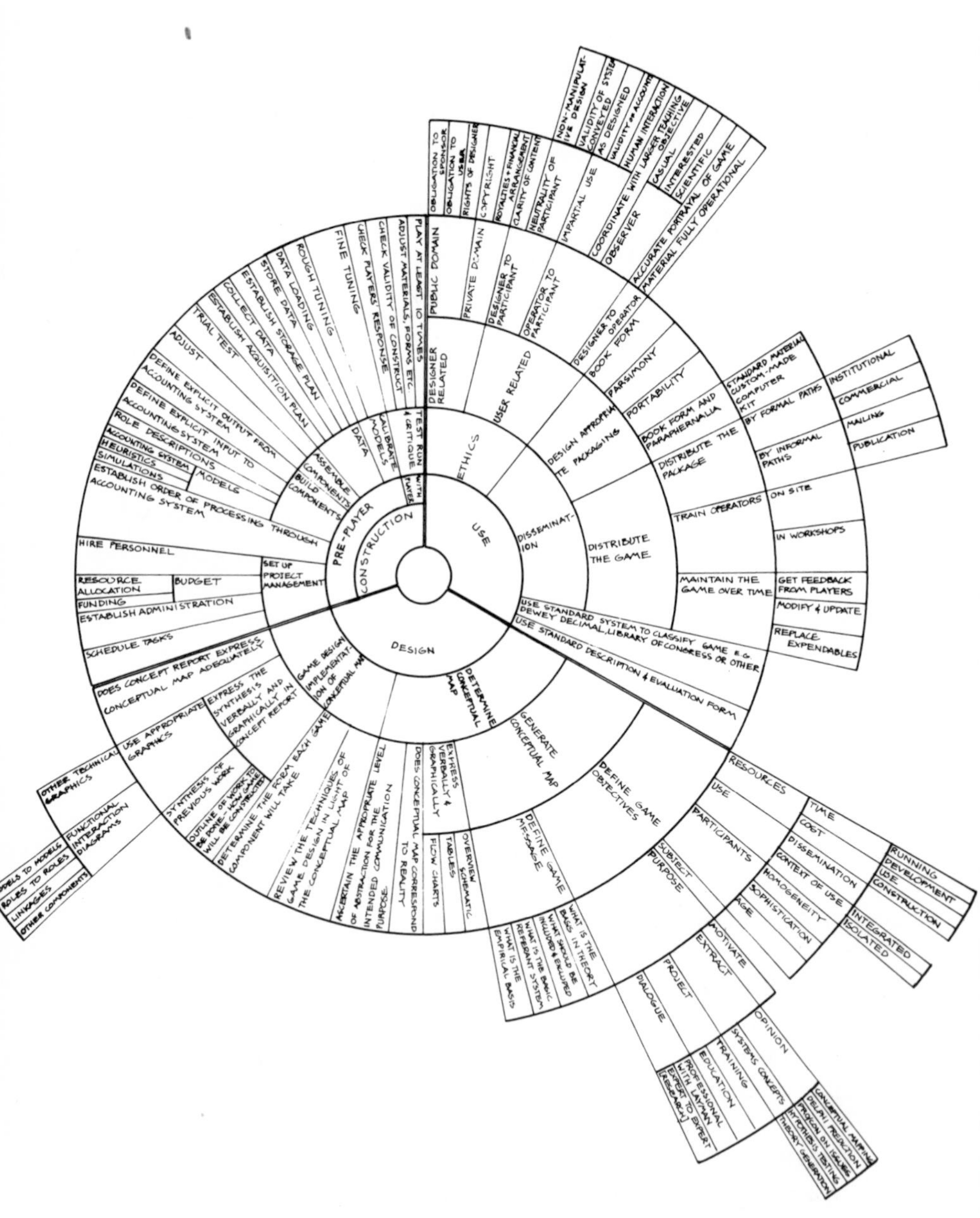

FIGURE 19.
The Game Design Process

DESIGN

The game design process consists of the process of design, construction, and use. Traditionally these three have not been distinguished. In practice they have overlapped and the subsequent confusion has resulted in a more costly product, a less satisfactory game, and a longer time between the inception of the game design process and the completion of the product. It is equally true that this confusion has produced many problems in the use of games. The design phase is the least understood, most underdeveloped, and most crucial of the entire design process. Game designers have often skipped the design phase to begin with the construction. This is like starting to build a house without a blueprint. Construction is normally a simple engineering task in which components are created, mechanically linked with the data base, and calibrated. By sidestepping the design stage, a game builder complicates and extends the construction stage, as well as makes it more expensive, less efficient, and less effective. Unfortunately, the design process requires that the designer address a series of questions which may be difficult to answer. To complete a design he needs a precise statement of the objective which prompts construction of the game in the first place.

Generate the Conceptual Map

Gaming is best understood as a communication form; an analysis of the various communications media indicates that each game is very specific to some precise communications purpose. This specificity of purpose as well as the high cost of the technique become convincing arguments for precision of the design and parsimony in the construction and use of the game. Two very powerful tools are available to meet these objectives—conceptual mapping and its interpreted expression through the gaming technique, the concept report.

Games are frequently employed for conveying complex systems. It is readily acknowledged that the system may not be understood at the time of game design, and that the purpose of the game may be to either extract concepts from a knowledgeable audience, or to assist some research team in the articulation of the system. In each case, the basic objective of the game should be expressed in a written document (text and/or graphics) to specify the conceptual map (either as it is to be conveyed, further articulated, or derived). Failure to achieve this will most likely lead to an ultimate lack of precision in the game product.

The express documentation of the conceptual map permits the systematic review of gaming considerations (repertoire of techniques, art, theory, and principles of design) to achieve the most effective game design for the particular purpose. Having achieved this end, it is highly desirable to commit this to writing (text, diagrams) in the form of a concept report before beginning construction. This serves two purposes: (1) it becomes a blueprint to guide the construction process; and (2) most importantly, it becomes the basis for evaluating the final product. If no documentation of purpose or objective exists, and no coherent review of gaming considerations is presented, the final game will not be subject to intelligent evaluation.

The conceptual map is an explicit, thorough, unambiguous, understandable, presentation of the system or gestalt which is being presented through the gaming/simulation. *Only upon the completion of an express statement of the conceptual map (text and graphics) should game design be initiated.*

The generation of the conceptual map entails the deliberate reflection upon game objectives and message. When these have been resolved, they are synthesized with game design principles. The report on this synthesis, the concept report, is a permanent record of the characteristics of the game to be designed, and an historical statement about the reasons for the choices made at the time the game design process began.

Define the Game Objectives

If you confront the designer of a game with the questions—Why was the game constructed? What was your purpose or objective in creating the game?—it is most probable that the response will be somewhat long-winded and indicate a multiple set of objectives, some of which are more clear than others. Most likely the predominant feature of the answer will be that the designer had a general sense that a game would be useful for presenting certain material to a particular audience. It is important, at this point, to make a sharp distinction between gaming/simulation which is intended to solve a communication problem and those games which are on the market for commercial purposes and are intended to make a profit. Sadly, the conceptual map represented by many of these commercial games is so heavily distorted in its simplification of reality that the audience making use of the game is almost certain to be misled about the true nature of the system or subject under consideration. There is a game on the market entitled *Square Mile* which is a commercial product with the prime purpose of amusing players. It converts the process of community planning into a very simple-minded random process which, while unfortunately mimicking true world planning in some instances, does a real disservice by conveying an inaccurate perception of what land planning actually is.

Purpose

It becomes paramount, therefore, to define the game objectives or purposes with clarity at the inception of the game design process. Actually, if these questions are answered— Is there a communications problem? Which communication medium is appropriate? What are the characteristics of the message to be conveyed? — then the purpose of the game will have been fairly well established. These game objectives should be tied into some broader context such as an academic situation, public service training program, or citizen participation program, where the game itself is one component of an organized format. There are four purposes for which gaming/simulation can be employed, and while it is most likely that one of these will be more dominant than the others, it seems probable that virtually all games will have two or more of these purposes evident in their structure.

Dialogue. The prime purpose of gaming/simulation is to establish dialogue to increase communication among a group about a topic which is complex, future-oriented, of a systems nature, and which requires a vocabulary or vernacular which is not commonly shared by the group at the outset of the discussion. There are several forms of dialogue which a game can permit:

(1) Expert to expert—this has often been demonstrated by interdisciplinary research teams who use gaming/simulation as a way of forming a more perfect communication about some idea or concept that is being pursued.

(2) Professional to a lay group—it is assumed that the professional starts with expert knowledge about a complex topic and now needs to transmit it to the layman in an understandable and efficient fashion. In the dialogue between the professional and the layman, it is implied that there would be a mutual advantage if the information shared by the layman could be assimilated with that shared by the professional.

(3) Layman to layman—about a topic which could not be dealt with through conventional forms of communication.

Project. The second purpose of gaming is to project information in an educational or training context. Perhaps the bulk of all games available today fall under this category, at least in terms of their main purpose; certainly this would seem to be the case with most educational, military, and business games, and many of the urban games. In any event, when the primary purpose is to project information, it is particularly incumbent on the game designer to have precisely defined and to have clearly presented the conceptual map, so that the potential user of the game is properly forewarned as to the potential utility of this game for his purpose.

Extract. A third purpose of gaming is to extract information or opinions from a group about the character of a system; in other words, to extract from some group their conceptual map of the problem at hand. In this sense, the game becomes the rough equivalent of a questionnaire. However, it is much more powerful than a questionnaire in that it becomes an opportunity to observe the response of an individual in context as opposed to the artificiality of the response normally associated with questionnaires.

There appear to be two areas in which games are used to extract information. The most significant has been in the area of system delineation. The outstanding example of a game technique being used operationally in this context is *Nexus*, developed by Robert Armstrong and Margaret Hobson of Birmingham, England. The *Nexus* technique is a systematic procedure for obtaining a specific commitment from professionals intimately familiar with the operating characteristics of a system. The system in question need not be an existing one, but may be hypothetical. Two researchers, Dr. Watson and Dr. Crick, who worked together on DNA were having some difficulty in communicating with each other about its molecular structure. To solve the problem they obtained a large supply of the children's game TinkerToy, and proceeded jointly to construct a large wooden framework which in their judgment was a conceptual representation of the basic DNA molecular structure. There can be no doubt that this iconic model was altered and realtered many times as they tried to improve their shared perceptions about a hypothetical statement which would serve to explain the behavior of the DNA molecular structure.

There are many examples of game/simulations which could satisfactorily be employed for hypothesis testing or theory generation. Perhaps the single greatest improvement to simulation would be to link carefully some of the better simulations to a good gaming exercise. Practical people with a realistic gestalt of the world (which includes more than can be incorporated in any simulation) could pragmatically test the relationships which develop in running these simulations. Such linking of good simulations with good games could result in better decisions in the area of public policy. For example, in the area of ecology (multiple or conflicting use such as estuaries or rivers) simulation gaming could be most valuable as a high level decisionmaking tool. There are several games under development which are moving in this direction. The *WALRUS* game being developed by Allan Feldt and David Moses for the Sea Grant Project is one of the better examples; an equally good example is the *SNAFOR* simulation being developed for the National Forest Service.

Another use of gaming is to extract opinion from the public or from other groups affected by a public or private decision which is pending and on which debate is being sought. Two games *Impasse?* and *At-Issue!* were recently developed for this purpose by Duke and Greenblat. These frame games permit the local user to generate a content which is appropriate to some local purpose, and to use a basic format which is consistent. The games are already in use as a way of recording public opinion from relatively large numbers of the public. They permit the citizen to indicate which considerations are the most important to him, and to state some numerical value indicating their relative importance. Such games include the opportunity for the participant to introduce his own material, whether it is an issue or the redefinition of the alternatives in the game.

Yet another category of games designed to extract opinion is that which is basically of the Delphi character. Several of these are in use by different authors. One very popular game used more as a parlor game than as a serious tool is *Future,* developed by Olaf Helmar and his associates.

Another example of using a game to extract opinion is the process of conceptual mapping (see Appendix B). Essentially, this is the process of creating a conceptual statement which defines some real or theoretical circumstance. The process is, in some ways, parallel to the two-dimensional mapping of geographic space represented by a highway map. If the problem is complex, then the effort of a team with different skills may be required to define the problem.

Motivate. The other purpose for which games are used is motivation. There are, in fact, some who would argue that this is the most frequent and most important use of gaming/simulation. This use is almost always linked with one or more of the three other purposes (dialogue, project, extract); but there are instances where motivation is the single objective of the game. One of the extraordinary things about gaming is the ability of even the worst of games to motivate the most recalcitrant and most unlikely audiences to "play" through a game which seemingly has little relevance. The ability to motivate is one of the central abilities of a good game. Stated conversely, a game which does not succeed well as a motivational tool has somehow failed badly as a gaming device. Some hunches about what makes a gaming experience a good motivational tool include: the more or less leaderless environment for learning; the rapid feedback mechanism; the opportunity to perform in roles which are normally denied in typical life situations; the relative freedom to experiment with ideas or situations which would be dangerous in the real world; the inherent childlike characteristic in all adults that lets us play games with glee and in playing be doubly pleased that we may be learning something. The fact that games are an innovative tool, and as such frequently a new experience, may be one of the motivational factors involved. The outstanding reason for motivation provided by a game is active participation in the communication process; virtually all other forms of communication require a passive receiver for extended periods of time. Games become live experiences, and it seems to be universally acknowledged that when they are properly achieved, motivation is an inevitable result. If there has ever been an age in which the bulk of mankind wants to be involved—to participate—that time is now.

Resources

In an earlier chapter, gaming/simulation was described as one of the most highly specific forms of communication available to man, one of the most recent, and, unfortunately, one of the most expensive. *Games are one of the most expensive modes of communication.* The expense of gaming has not yet been clearly acknowledged, but would be revealed dramatically if it were really possible to do cost-benefit analysis, especially in consideration of the widespread misuse of gaming. Many games currently available in an academic context would suffer rather badly in any cost-benefit analysis, and this is particularly true for some of the more massive (that is, expensive) games. The assumption is that virtually all games are run for at least two categories of persons: (1) groups that are in some sense anticipated and intended at the time of the original design; and (2) groups which happen along as serendipitous targets. Most games, unfortunately, have a much larger experience with the second type of audiences. This seems to be particularly true of the large expensive games, the so-called multiple purpose games.

When considering resources for game design, both cost and time are essential factors. The resources required to design, construct, test, and disseminate the game must be considered, as well as the cost encountered each time the game is used. Unless you have had previous experience with games, you may be startled to realize the range of costs for construction and use of different games. Some of the more colossal urban games probably have true costs of construction in excess of a million dollars and an average cost for each use of several thousand dollars. A word of caution is needed here—the definition of what constitutes cost must be carefully considered. For example, in the construction of *METRO–APEX* the funds available for that project were $170,000 from the federal agency of Housing and Urban Development (HUD). It was, however, agreed that the project would "piggyback" on top of a large 701 study being conducted simultaneously in the Tri-County Regional Planning Commission of Lansing, Michigan for which funds in excess of a million dollars were being spent. The team developing *METRO–APEX* literally moved into the offices of the regional planning agency conducting the HUD studies and were active participants in the design and formation of those studies. Furthermore, simulation models were borrowed (with permission) from other communities. Attempts to unravel the true cost of the development must also include student efforts which are often heroic and unpaid, as well as the professional effort which is frequently a labor of love. Therefore, simple-minded statements that a particular game cost "X" dollars should be examined with care; it is often to the advantage of the commentator to over or underinflate the cost in order to prove some point about the utility of games.

A game may cost as little as one or two manpower-days or may run into hundreds of thousands of dollars. Games often cost many times the initial estimates, particularly when precise goals are not stated and approved by the client before construction begins. Similarly, the cost of using a game may vary greatly. With costs so difficult to estimate, it is incumbent on the client and designer to agree on precisely what resources will be made available during construction and for normal use of the game. Many game designers have given their client a product of reduced utility because the unit cost per run was beyond the capacity of the organization to sustain. The client should demand of the designer that the cost of typical use of the game not exceed a certain level. Such a demand might be a performance standard governing payment for game construction. Such a penalty will almost certainly result in the game designer being more precise about the cost of use. The type of use of the game will have a significant bearing on the cost. If each use of the game has a new audience and a new game operator, the cost will remain high. In those instances where the game will be used frequently by the same highly trained operator and where the audiences are highly consistent, the cost will fall off markedly. Evaluation should be on the basis of standard use rather than initial trials which always tend to be more costly.

Allocation of time is no less important than dollars both in development and running of a game. There is a tendency for game designers to become overly elaborate in game design: for example, excessive level of the detail presented; sophistication of the simulations employed for various calculations; quantity of data presented to the players before or during play; failure to rely on conventional communication devices for major elements of the training. The time required for the development of a game will be largely the product of several factors: first, the clarity with which the problem has been stated; second, the appropriateness of the problem for gaming/simulation as a communication form; third, the specification of goals in a concept report approved by the client group; fourth, the range of skill and experience of the game designer(s). The designer must possess three types of skills: a knowledge of the literature on gaming/simulation; a personal familiarity with a wide range of games gained through actual use; and, extensive experience in the running of games under a variety of circumstances. No single factor is more useful in training potential game designers than the actual successful running of games, repeatedly and under different circumstances.

Careful thought must also be given to the time required to run a game. Time may be constrained by the desired cost of a run (the amount of money available to pay operators and computer time) or by the context in which the game is played (time available away from usual school or office activities). The nature of the game experience can vary considerably from a single afternoon adventure to a week-long workshop to a semester-long course. *Games, whether in design, construction or use, will absorb all time and resources available.*

Subject

The subject of a game must be specified in the most precise way. The specification of substantive content may take the form of written reports, abstracts, or detailed subject outline. The client who commissions a game without some such document may discover that the final product is not relevant to his purpose. If, however, the client requires a game which can be used for a variety of problem situations, an exception can be made. The frame game is intended to be subject-less. It is intended to be loaded with a subject by the operator (and/or participants) at the time of play. Although a frame game is designed to create a particular situation, the subject matter or content of a frame game will be routinely altered or replaced to meet the needs of the client. Examples of games whose content is methodically replaced by players are *Impasse?*, *At-Issue!*, *Nexus*, and *Policy Negotiations.*

Participants

Equally important to the clear expression of message or purpose is the careful definition of intended audience. Surely Dr. Seuss's formal written transmission to other adults would not be recognizable to the children who love his popular books. The game is more occasion-specific than any other form of communication. It is imperative for a game designer to have in mind his intended audience, their motivations for participation, and the typical conditions of use. The more precisely the game designer has articulated his message or purpose, audience characteristics, motivations, and pragmatic considerations controlling the use of his product, the more effectively he can employ various design considerations to ensure a successful game and the more certain he can be that gaming is the appropriate media choice.

Before the concept report is complete, it should include a detailed section specifying the intended participants in terms of age, level of sophistication, homogeneity, prior training, prior shared experiences, and prerequisite language forms (for example, mathematics or computer programming) required before being permitted to play the game. In short, the concept report should note any characteristic of the participant group which would have a bearing on game design.

Use

When defining the game, its objectives and characteristics, careful thought should be given to the context of use of the final product. Is it to be an isolated and free-standing product employed randomly as the occasion may demand? Is it an integrated part of an academic curriculum? Will it be employed in a public relations program? Or for citizen use in discussions of public policy? Most games will be of greatest value when used as one of a variety of communication forms in an integrated format in some larger context.

Another problem that must be addressed when considering the use of the game is dissemination. If the task of reproduction and distribution of game paraphernalia is as involved as that of training operators, the game designer may find himself in a situation where there are not sufficient funds to meet the demands, despite a strong ethical and professional desire to respond to requests. It becomes imperative, therefore, at the time of the conception of the game to anticipate what method will be used for dissemination and what charge, if any, will be made for use of the game, game materials, or operator training. This topic should be covered in detail in the concept report. If attention is addressed to this problem at the time of game design, clever techniques might minimize the cost and trouble of dissemination.

Define Game Message

A game message is quite different from any message conveyed by other media in the communications continuum. Historically, these other communication forms have dealt with problems in a sequential format or, if they dealt with problems as gestalt situations, they presented them as two-dimensional experiences aimed at a passive observer. A game message is significantly different in that it attempts to define a multidimensional, simultaneous, systemic, complex, and interactive situation. The message to be transmitted must be clearly defined if it is not to be garbled in transmission. Anyone who has had experience with the telegraph industry in recent years knows how difficult it is using a fairly straightforward, simplistic, and highly sequential form to get even the simplest messages from point A to point B and back.

The game designer often fails to have the message clearly in mind at the outset which results in an ambiguous product. The most clever designers sometimes hide this flaw successfully by suggesting the game for a multiplicity of purposes, leaving the choice of application to the operator. Some game designers, however, have attempted to state with clarity, prior to construction, the nature of the message to be conveyed. Using texts and schematics, they state both the theoretical and empirical basis involved. The conceptual map may be explicit, implicit or integral. The explicit conceptual map addresses the question of the game message openly, deliberately, and clearly, using text and graphics. The implicit conceptual map suggests that, subsequent to play, a critical review by the players would reveal a clear picture of the game message. The integral conceptual map embeds the message directly into the play of the game; by the process of entering into the game the player is exposed directly to it. One example of such a technique employs a flow chart of the process being investigated as part of the game paraphernalia; the players manipulate the system by altering the flow chart to experiment with alternate forms of management. *A conceptual map must be supported by empirical data and appropriate theoretical evidence. A game always contains a conceptual map, either explicit, implicit (conscious or unconscious), or integral.*

After the game message has been clearly designated, it is necessary to specify the theory which supports the message. This is no different than using lectures, films, or other communication modes. It is difficult to believe that, pound for pound, more baloney is processed through games than through training films or lectures. Conversely, it seems that the game designer has an unusual opportunity to document carefully the theoretical basis for the multidimensional gestalt being pursued. If there is a lack of theory, this should be presented with equal candor so that those dealing with the problem will have some notion where reality ends and fantasy begins.

A problem of very similar dimension is that of the empirical base on which the game message is formulated. There has been a great amount of hokum in the past decade about urban data bases at the "small area" (census tract) level under the general heading of data banks. Few, if any, such data banks are operational except for very specialized administrative purposes, and, therefore, data derived from such sources must be used with the greatest of caution. Obtaining a thorough, valid, data base can be a costly, painful and time-consuming process which few simulators and even fewer gamers are inclined to address. As a result, the empirical data generally available to urban gamers tends to be something of a crude amalgamation of a generalized American city. For other gamers, data may be more or less crude. It becomes, then, a serious obligation on the part of the game designer to state in some detail in the concept report the precise form of empirical data available, its source, its probable validity, the nature of any checks conducted to establish validity, and comparisons with other data sources which would indicate the extent to which it has been fudged.

When dealing with the multidimensional world of gaming, fudging becomes one of the implied central arts. The art of "muddling through" has been evident in the social sciences for some time. In gaming/simulation, data which is artificially generated can become a source of strength if it is presented with candor rather than through subterfuge. If nothing else, the admission of fudge work may motivate someone to search out more valid data, and thereby in later versions of the game allow the replacement of guesswork with fact.

Express the Conceptual Map with Text and Graphics

The issues previously raised must be resolved in order to form a conceptual map which describes what the game is to be. As a first step toward writing the concept report, the conceptual map, which represents the goals of the game as a communication device, should be clearly stated by text and graphics. The conceptual map can then be reviewed before being subjected to design activities. *The game may be employed as a device to formulate the conceptual map, and, hence, suggest the conceptual base and/or empirical evidence required to sustain it.* (The questions which must be answered in order to compose an adequate conceptual map are summarized in Appendix A.)

Correspondence of Conceptual Map to Reality

During review of the conceptual map, one question in particular should be paramount: Does the conceptual map correspond to reality sufficiently well to meet the needs of the client? Differences on this point must be resolved prior to game construction. Failure to do so will result in decisions on critical issues being made by lower level technicians rather than the designer who should be making them. Any alterations of the game message during the construction phase will necessitate expensive modifications.

Ascertain the Appropriate Level of Abstraction

The final and most significant question to be addressed during the evaluation of the conceptual map is whether the level of abstraction proposed for the game design is appropriate for the intended communication purpose. It is probable that this question will cause more serious problems than any of those raised above. The question should not be left to assistants; rather, a group of experts and potential users should address the question. The team should point out what impact changes in level of abstraction will have on such factors as cost or duration of the game during both construction and use. Also, this technical staff can point out some problems associated with later modifications and additions to the game if the level of abstraction is too detailed, which is frequently the case. One way to avoid this problem is to design a series of games of increasing detail; the first merely introduces the players to the game language and the following game(s) serve the major purposes of the game.

The level of abstraction of the game message is a difficult area. Obviously, the many questions raised earlier in this chapter will help in the definition of the areas to be emphasized. However, there will be many areas for which the arguments for inclusion or exclusion are highly debatable; ultimately, these will be decided upon some arbitrary bases. The final concept report should indicate the reasons for the decision. The choice of any media implies some criteria by which we abstract that which is transmitted. This results in a reduction of material transmitted, a partial statement of reality. The level of abstraction must be carefully reviewed and approved by the client; failure to do so may result in a crisis when the game is finally put into play. If, in the judgment of the client and/or participants, the problem is expressed at an inappropriate level for their purposes, the product will be a failure. If the arguments relative to the level of abstraction are stated in the concept report, dissatisfaction may be avoided. *The most critical element of game design is the choice of an appropriate level of abstraction.*

Implementation of the Conceptual Map Through Game Design

It is now incumbent on the game designer to review both the "Repertoire of Techniques" (Chapter 7) and "Game Components" (Chapter 6). When utilizing techniques extracted from known games or drawn from the imagination of the designers, it is necessary to develop a coordinated design which synthesizes the objectives described in the conceptual map. This synthesis of conceptual map and gaming techniques is expressed in a concept report, which is subject to review by the client and others.

Game designers have usually approached the construction, testing, and use of their game in a sequential fashion. This wasteful process might be improved upon by the designer first establishing in his mind the conceptual map to be conveyed. The message (gestalt) is then to be reviewed in the light of techniques of game design (Figure 19), which entails a deliberate appraisal, sector by sector, against the notions represented by the game design wheel. This results in a synthesis of the client's purpose, conceptual map, game objectives, subject matter, resources, participants, and the context of use of the game. The synthesis forms a blueprint for the process of construction. To the extent the concept report avoids critical issues, begs questions, fails to address redundancies, hides the facts about inadequate data, or glosses over real differences in perception between what is possible in game design and what is desired by the client, the concept report will only serve to delay the subsequent process of game construction.

In addition to the synthesis described above, the concept report has an obligation to outline the procedures for construction. This phase of the concept report must show all of the final components as they are to exist individually, including their purpose and style; it must indicate the data and its specific use; it must show the order of sequence of any processing that will take place, either in or out of a computer; it must show both macro-level and micro-level cycles of play; and it should include flow charts which are sufficiently detailed to be adequate for the use of those building individual components.

The use of graphics throughout the concept report

is essential, including functional interaction diagrams which show the relationship from one model to all other models, from a given role to all other roles, from a particular component or data source to all other data sources, and from all of the linkages implied above—model to role, role to component, component to model—in all meaningful combinations (see Figure 20). In addition to being presented as static diagrams, they should also be presented as diagrams showing the dynamic relationships which are being sought. Other technical graphics should be used to assist in forming a game-specific language.

Certainly no single inclusion can be of greater value than a mock-up of all game materials, including diagrams of boards, markers, and so on, as well as the decision forms for player use. There are two reasons for this: (1) these are very difficult to prepare, and if successfully presented at this stage, the client can be more certain that the level of detail is appropriate; (2) these materials reveal to the client a great deal about the final character of the game. As a result, attention must be focused on these materials during the review process.

Before the concept report is judged to be complete, careful review by the staff, the intended users, the technical review committee, and the client should be completed. *The formal completion of a concept report before construction begins will enhance the quality of the final game.*

CONSTRUCTION

Many professional gamers like to bypass the first two sectors of game design, and jump headlong into construction. As a consequence, there may be failure to achieve precision of design, the careful engineering of the construct to meet some precise communication need, and almost certainly a loss of parsimony in the construction activities themselves. Nonetheless, there are two reasonable explanations of this tendency to begin in the middle. First, the concept of games as a problem-specific language yielding to orderly rules of design has not been generally recognized; and second, it is hard work

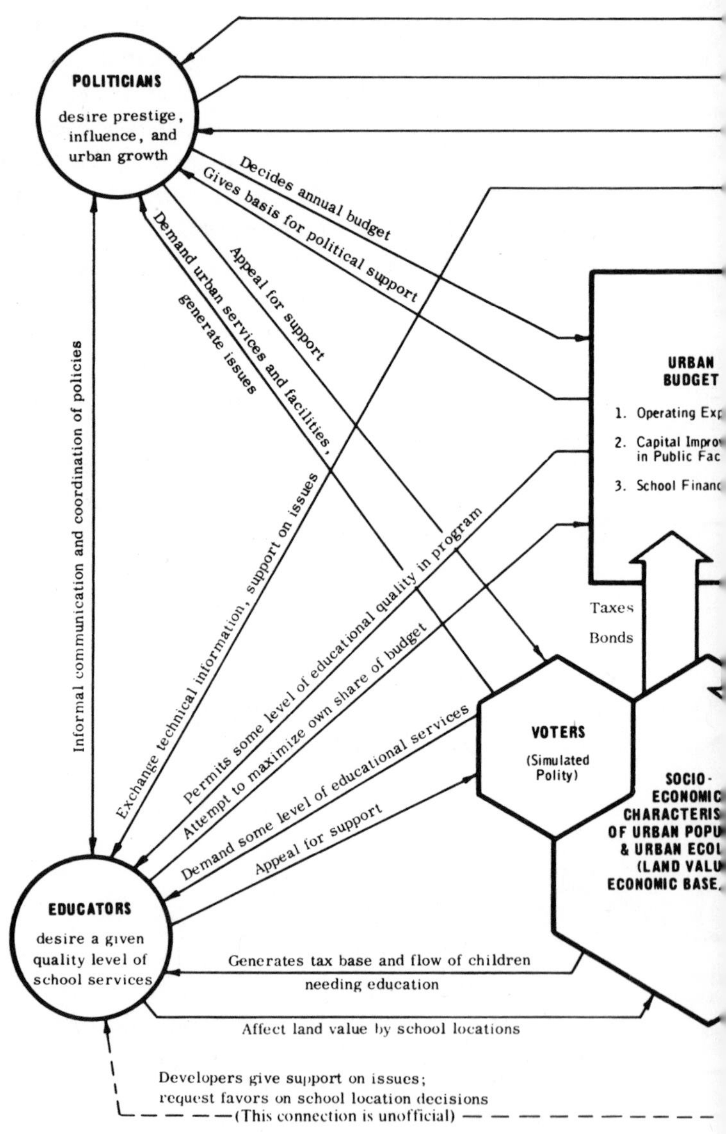
POLITICIANS
desire prestige, influence, and urban growth
Decides annual budget
Gives basis for political support
Appeal for support
Demand urban services and facilities, generate issues
Informal communication and coordination of policies
Exchange technical information, support on issues
Permits some level of educational quality in program
Attempt to maximize own share of budget
Demand some level of educational services
Appeal for support
URBAN BUDGET
1. Operating Exp
2. Capital Impro in Public Fac
3. School Financ
Taxes
Bonds
VOTERS
(Simulated Polity)
SOCIO-ECONOMIC CHARACTERIS OF URBAN POPU & URBAN ECOL (LAND VALU ECONOMIC BASE,
EDUCATORS
desire a given quality level of school services
Generates tax base and flow of children needing education
Affect land value by school locations
Developers give support on issues; request favors on school location decisions
(This connection is unofficial)

FIGURE

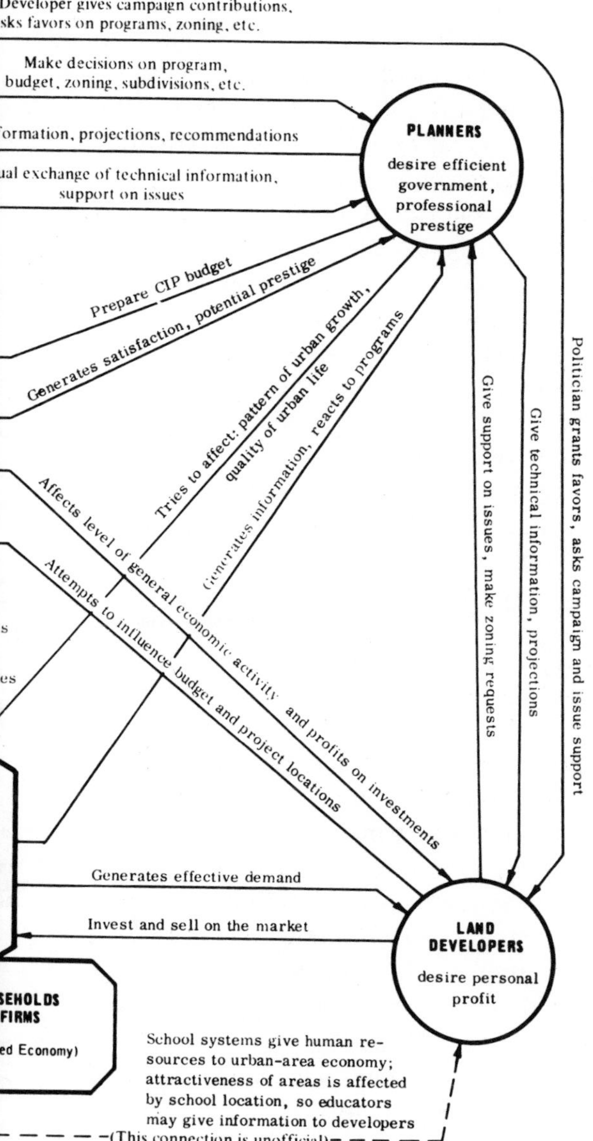

SOURCE: Richard D. Duke (1966) *METRO: A Gaming Simulation.* METRO Project Report No. 5 Lansing, Mich.: Tri-County Regional Planning Commission.

TRO Functional Interactions

to answer all the questions that must be raised to establish detailed game specifications, and the difficulty is compounded by the element of risk inherent in making a written commitment which might later serve as an indictment of the author. The process of constructing a game inevitably forces the designer to confront these questions anyway, although in a less systematic way. Part of the art of good game construction lies in the ability to make a simultaneous solution of many variables. And so, as recognized earlier, we can expect the designer to benefit from an orderly and sequential concept of game design, even though in practice many liberties may be taken.

If a gaming project is of any magnitude, various project management mechanisms may be required. Note that if proper care has been taken in developing the concept report, construction can be a highly organized and efficient process employing standard management practice. If, however, construction is coterminus with an effort in determining objectives and methodology to be employed, at least marginal chaos is to be expected.

Construction, in either case, entails identifiable components (boards, paraphernalia, models, and so on), the collection of data required for loading (if necessary), and their joint assembly into an initial (usually rudimentary) game. This must be carefully subjected to calibration and evaluation before release for professional use. Countless hours of participant time have been squandered with immature game products. These often result in the unnecessary aggravation of a captive audience, and sometimes bring about the permanent alienation of some players from the gaming technique. This phase, even more than those preceding it, requires that attention be deliberately redirected to the basic game objectives in order to maximize the final fit of the game.

If the concept report has been adequately prepared, reviewed, and modified, it becomes the blueprint for the construction of the game. Construction, under these circumstances, becomes quite straightforward; it involves a set of activities undertaken before the players are introduced and a second set with the players participating. Pre-player activity entails the constructing and assembling of the various components, and rough calibration.

The larger the game the more intricate the management scheme must be. There must be a clear hierarchy in terms of management with proper procedures for resolving differences of opinion. Routine passing of decisions before a technical review board is good policy, and the preparation of *internal reports* for working purposes is useful. The administrative structure should be established at the earliest point, with responsibility for personnel, budget, general administration, and subject content resolved as early as possible.

Budget may be a major consideration. Careful attention should be given particularly to the true date of availability of funds, the duration over which the funds are available, possibilities of extension if delays are encountered, and possibilities of additional funding if problems are encountered. Even in relatively small projects it is an excellent idea to have a simple budget account system which lists all possible expenditures. A listing of initial allocations as approved by the funding agency, monthly expenditures, encumbrances, and balance remaining may prove useful. The size and nature of the project will govern the extent of the system, but some techniques may help to avoid a crisis of exhausted funds before the project is completed.

A general rule of operation is "the funds available are always less than the funds required." This somewhat cynical expression simply acknowledges there will seldom be enough money to build a game with quite the luxury desired. For this reason, it is important to establish a resource allocation system at the outset and to make periodic checks to see that the scheme is not being violated. The basic scheme is to have a schedule of specific tasks assigned both in terms of dollars and manpower. Some type of time scheduling system will also be required. Even with careful budgeting, scheduling of tasks, estimation of resources, and frequent checking, misallocations may occur. This may require a decision to delete certain components from the original design.

Personnel selection may prove difficult because

there are few people with extensive experience. Therefore, consideration should be given to subcontracting the various tasks. This has two advantages: unless there is performance, the project is saved the cost; and an opportunity is provided to gain experience with staff who will potentially be hired on a more permanent basis. For the resolution of difficult problems such as those dealing with basic theory or the definition of the conceptual map, consideration should be given to hiring a consultant.

One procedure that may prove useful is the development of internal reports. These papers are prepared for each aspect of the game and are strictly for internal use. Under no circumstances are they to be released beyond the project until reviewed as a formal project report. The benefit of these internal reports is that a written record is formulated as the game takes shape; they become invaluable when questions arise about the character of work undertaken.

Order of Processing

The single most important element in game construction is the establishment of the order of processing all inputs through the accounting system. A system is a gestalt, yet an *accounting system* is inevitably sequential. It requires sophisticated judgments to ensure that the actual order of processing (sequential) results in an experience by the participant of a system (gestalt). If the game is to be processed on a computer, this consideration is quite imperative because processing is highly sequential.

Build Components

The basic construction technique for games is to identify in advance a series of components, presumably governed by a logic which manipulates inputs and generates outputs either for use by other components or by the players. The careful delineation of these components before construction is essential. All components should be named, identified, and described with the inputs and their sources and character. Theoretical and empirical bases should be carefully described, with particular attention to the quality of empirical data. Finally, the output to be generated by each component should be described (its character, purpose, and intended use).

Models

The construction of models includes the construction of accounting systems, simulations and heuristics. There must be a balance in detail, character and content between all of the many components as they are finally presented to the player. As a general rule, the simulation to be employed should be the least involved to convey the required level of detail. There is a risk that a simulation too harshly restricted becomes compromised, and that its decreased authenticity fails to convey an accurate gestalt. Decisions pertaining to the level of detail should be made in the context of the communication objectives. Overall balance must have a greater integrity than that of a particular simulation.

Models take three forms in a gaming/simulation: accounting systems, simulations, and heuristics. By accounting systems what is meant is the factual representation of some real-world process at an acceptable level of detail for use in the context of the gestalt of the game. As such, accounting systems are neither predictive nor speculative; rather, they are clear and precise abstractions of processes which are known in the real world, and which have been defined previously with sufficient clarity to permit their judicious abstraction for gaming purposes. A typical example would be the process of raising city revenues through property taxes, which would include a series of known steps starting with the evaluation of real property, the definition of the rules under which that value would be converted to assessed value, the definition of the process by which millage or tax rates are set, and the application of this millage against the assessed value of the property to produce a total revenue. These are basically repetitive mechanical tasks.

Simulations, on the other hand, are theoretical

speculations about the character of some complex process. Their logic is predicated on a series of evaluations of empirical data so that the output of a simulation should be scientifically defensible. Because they are intended to predict they are very useful in gaming/simulations which are frequently oriented toward the resolution of "what if" types of questions.

The third type of model is a substitute for simulation. Heuristics are frequently used in gaming as temporary measures in lieu of valid simulations. The function of the heuristic is to accept input and produce output comparable to that which would be expected of a simulation. They are not predictive, but simply a crude abstraction of some complex process.

One of the single most important uses of heuristics is during the construction of a gaming/simulation, if the components are candidly identified and their limits acknowledged. Their use permits establishment of a gestalt about a complex problem—as long as the players understand that certain components are crude speculations. The advantages of this method are that it permits continued study of the problem and that it easily permits replacement of a given heuristic with a more accurate simulation.

Define the Explicit Inputs and Outputs to and from the Accounting System

Before construction of each game component, it is necessary to explicitly define what that component will generate. This becomes input to be processed. Conversely, when input to the accounting system from other components is processed, it becomes accounting system output which in turn may become input to the original component. Two problems are encountered: first, the level of detail (the purpose of the total game is to present a gestalt about a complex problem and each of the components should provide information at a level appropriate to the total gestalt being sought); second, the overall level of complexity resulting from these linkages. The objective of the game designer is to select those components which must be linked to serve the communication need. It will be necessary to define and redefine these linkages as the process of construction nears completion.

It is possible to have complex linkages within the computer, but the human brain can only deal with a limited set. The test, then, is whether the inclusion of a particular linkage offers significant information to the gestalt. Additionally, consideration must be given to the limits of human comprehension.

Assemble Components

The moment of truth is at hand; and the probabilities are very high that you are in for a disappointment. If the game has much complexity, the final assembly and trial tests of the total system will yield a variety of failures, omissions, overlaps, inadequacies, trivia, redundancies, inanities, and just plain errors. Time should be reserved for the linking and assembling of the various components in order to permit their modification and adjustment. The need for fudge factors may appear, and if so, research must be done to establish a logical basis on which to calibrate these factors. It is always incumbent on the game designer to document the introduction of a fudge factor and explain the logic supporting the factor employed. If this is done, there will be an opportunity later to remove this fudge factor either because of improved theory, improved data, or the location of errors originally overlooked. In a computer game there is a tendency for errors to appear as a result of misinterpretations of the designer's intent by the computer programmer.

Data

The classical chicken and egg problem reappears under a new guise here. Without data we would have no theory from which to establish a general notion of the system; yet the acquisition of data without some previously established theory can result in data acquired for its own sake. The data question has been held off until this point in the game design process to ensure that the designer has thought through the reasons for building a game, its objectives, and its character. Obviously, to have arrived at this point a great deal of data has been reviewed.

The design process discussed earlier begins to define the data needs for the game. In the process of responding to the questions which have been raised the game designer will have become quite familiar with sources of data, including those which must be gathered specifically for this game. The basic rule to bear in mind at this point is parsimony.

It is important to establish an acquisition plan for the collection of data. The plan should include definition of the data items, sources of each item, rules for determining accuracy to be applied during the process of collection, guidelines for sampling procedures, and similar considerations. It is also necessary to establish a storage plan: the specific definition and documentation of each data item collected, its sources and limitations, its rules for storage and conversion to digital form (if required) as well as for manipulation if the data is not to be used in its raw form. All data under consideration for collection must have a place in the processing of the game itself. Failure to identify a bona fide use will indicate that the data are unnecessary or that a component is improperly defined. A final step, after the data has been collected, manipulated, and converted to the appropriate mechanical form, is the loading into the assembled components.

Calibrate the Components

Calibrating components involves two stages, rough and fine tuning. Each individual component should be processed a number of times to show that within general margins of acceptability it is functioning as expected. After the various components are linked together, the entire system should be run until it can be shown that the product is within levels of specification. The second stage requires more finesse because of the need to establish balance between components. At this stage, the game is a potpourri of data and models, and it will not be easy to pinpoint the component which requires adjustment. There is a very strong temptation to do the simplest thing: fudge the final product. To yield to this temptation may result in a basic error in the logic, construction, or data collection and manipulation.

If the process of fine tuning gives unsatisfactory results, the staff should apply themselves diligently to discover why the error exists before simple "fudging" is permitted. There should be very strict rules prohibiting "fudging" without the explicit approval of the project manager; all such changes should be recorded.

Construction Activities with Test Players Present

The completed game must be put to the test with actual participants. In the earliest runs the players will probably be those who helped design it, those who have some particular stake in the game, or those who fit into a category of "sympathetic players" (those who understand that it is a test vehicle and will be willing to continue play even though difficulties are encountered). The process of critiquing and final calibration with players goes through three basic stages. The first is the attempt to complete one cycle with cooperative players until everything appears to be generally in order. The second phase is the attempt to complete a series of cycles constituting an entire game at least three to five times until it appears that all of the bugs have been worked out of the game. The final phase is governed by the "rule of ten." *A game should be presented as complete only after it has been tested with appropriate audiences on ten separate occasions, the final three of which should require no further adjustment or modification of the game.*

The client, the participants, and the game designers must recognize that many different runs may be required before the game itself is finally and completely calibrated. Depending on the primary purpose of the game and the character of the system involved, there may never be a time when a "final" game exists. Instead, there may be continuous modifications after an analysis of each game run in order to adjust the construct so that it more closely resembles the product desired.

During the testing of the game with players, care should be taken to observe player response to roles and, in particular, the response to the game-specific language which the players must learn. Almost inevitably, early runs reveal unnecessary detail or a vernacular which is more technical than is necessary. Listen to the players and pay particular attention to their complaints about the materials they are dealing with. After all, you are attempting to construct a language which will improve their ability to deal with a complex problem. If your best efforts are confusing to the player, you have the painful task of doing it over again.

During these test runs the general question of balance and flow of activities should be considered with care. Is any player finished with his activities well in advance of other players? Are several players attempting to obtain the same information simultaneously, and competing with one another unnecessarily for documentation? Are the responses of the players truly representative of their intentions? Is the process of conversion from a player's written form to a calculation form simple, straightforward and error-free? Are problems of timing worked out so that the players are given appropriate amounts of time to preview material, to review past cycle output, to discuss with one another inter-team and intra-team the decisions which are facing them in this cycle? Is there adequate time for critique? Are the players at the completion of the exercise dissatisfied and, if so, what is the cause? Are the players motivated to pursue the problem beyond the game experience?

Finally, and most importantly, during critiques as the game is being tested, what is the reaction of the sophisticated player to the gestalt encountered in the game vis-a-vis the real-world counterpart which it presumes to represent? Anyone with extensive gaming experience has encountered the deflating remark, "It was a lot of fun but it is just not like that in the real world." If this proves to be the case, the game has failed its purpose and further modification is essential.

During the rule of ten runs, it is advisable to introduce very sophisticated players for the last three runs, and to play the game strictly according to Hoyle. This means paying close attention to their reactions, and during the critique period pursuing in-depth any reservations they may have about the balance, level of detail, relevance, vernacular employed, models, maintaining player interest, speed of play, or any other area of comment. There is probably no better test of the validity of a particular game than its acceptance by a sophisticated audience who are already known to be reasonably familiar with the gestalt which is being presented by the game.

PUTTING THE COMPLETED GAME INTO USE

When a game has passed the rule of ten, its designer must consider ethics, dissemination, classification, description, and evaluation. These problems should be recognized and solved as part of the design and construction of any particular game. Game design can be viewed as a "happening" in many instances. If this is true of the design of games, it is unfortunately doubly true of many game runs, even though the game itself is cleverly conceived and carefully executed and tested. What is the underlying cause?

If we substitute "book" for "game" we have a clue to this failure. Very sophisticated systems exist and are in routine and widespread use, which enables "book" to be identified and secured (readily finding the fifty that might be relevant to your problem out of a library of perhaps a million). Common practices allow reasonably precise evaluation on the grounds of appropriateness, validity of content, and so on, simply by examination of the physical object "book." Returning to "game," we find no useful parallels—whoever understood the *game* of Monopoly by reading the dreary and endless rules presented in fine print? In short, we have not, as a profession, developed interpretive criteria that are in common usage. The gamer must trust luck, hoping to improve his batting average through experience and personal contacts.

Three interpretive criteria must be established as routine convention among gamers.

(1) A taxonomic system must be employed for filing purposes. This can be done simply by endorsing some existing system currently in use for books.

(2) A brief written abstract in standard format should reveal design specifications and the author's purpose, subject, and

intended context of use. Remember, the game is a highly specific communication device—if the author did not know where *he* was aiming, how do *you* know what you will hit?

(3) Standard procedures must be formulated to assist reviewers in evaluating games for institutional endorsement, individual selection for one time use, or game review purpose in journals.

Ethical Considerations

Of increasing urgency is a sense of ethical responsibility for the product, both in its design and use. Academic tradition and legal precedent are probably adequate for any commercial versions that may be involved—Is the product in the public domain or private property? Has adequate courtesy been given to those whose games were aped? and so on. These are the responsibility of the designer and yield readily to standard convention. But new ethical problems may emerge in the *use* of a game and these are always the responsibility of the operator, although in many cases this responsibility must be shared by the designer. If the designer's conceptual map is a speculation, an alternative to be explored, should it be presented as reality? What are the obligations to the player(s) to avoid injury that occurs beyond the game environment? Ethical questions of gaming are only now beginning to emerge—each designer shares the responsibility for careful thought.

Designer-Related Ethics

The designer must establish at the outset whether his game is in the public or private domain. While this may be obvious in some instances, it will frequently be difficult to resolve. The bulk of games in use at the present time have been generated by people in academic or other public institutions. Often, the funding for these has been from clearly established sources which place the final product in the public domain. Sometimes, the game is generated spontaneously by the faculty member using time and resources of his own.

The rights of the game designer should be addressed in the concept report. Is the product when returned to the client to be an anonymous creation, or is the author to be identified? One of the traditional rewards for academic endeavor has been publication through traditional communication forms. Similar recognition for game designers seems appropriate.

In the case of games which are essentially in the private domain, the ethical questions seem to be resolved by mimicking those procedures associated with the production of books and similar materials. Copyright, patent, trademark laws, and general procedures for royalties already employed for books can readily be transferred for use with games.

User-Related Ethics

Ethical problems relating to users—that is, participants and operators—are becoming even more apparent than those relating to designers. In virtually all areas of experimentation where humans are used as subjects, whether for medical or psychological purposes, clearly defined ethical conventions have been or are being formulated. Since games entail demands on individuals in terms of time, cost, and psychological resources, it is incumbent upon the profession to develop an ethical code governing appropriate use of games. There are three areas which should be addressed: obligations of the designer to the participants, obligations of the operator to the participants, and obligations of the designer to the operator.

Designer to Participant. The designer of a game has an obligation to the game participants to present them with a game of clear content. The conceptual map must be presented with sufficient clarity so that participants, having expended the time and energy required by the game, will be capable of understanding its content. Failure to achieve this is failure of the game to communicate. This is another argument for the initial, clear designation of the problem and identification of the audience by the designer early in the design process.

The game designer has a further obligation to produce a nonmanipulative, neutral design. By neutrality of design what is meant is that there must be safeguards against the game designer constructing a situation which is self-serving, whether self be the designer or the client. This may best be achieved by requiring prominent display of the client and/or sponsor, particularly when the game is of a commercial character. The question of nonmanipulative design is difficult to deal with. The game should be presented to the audience in good faith rather than as a subterfuge through which other purposes are being pursued. For example, if a game purports to be in use to convey information but is really being used as a psychological testing device, basic ethical principles have been violated.

Finally, the validity of the system conveyed must be established in some reasonable form. If a concept report has been prepared subject to the reviews suggested earlier and if the game has been designed to accurately reflect that conceptual map, there would seem to be some guarantee of validity. Conversely, if the system is hypothetical, or the independent opinion of a particular observer, it can be so identified before commencement of play.

Operator to Participant. It is necessary at this point to distinguish between the designer and the operator. While in the early stages of most games they are the same individual, there is usually a rapid dispersal of the game and the operators may be temporally and spatially far removed from the designer. In these situations, the designer can no longer be held to account for all ethical considerations and the game operator becomes largely responsible. The operator will not have been privy to the thought that went into the development of the concept report and game construction. The operator is, therefore, required to familiarize himself with the details of the game before attempting runs for serious purposes. The operator must make impartial use of the game; the game should be used for the purposes and in the manner for which it was designed. The operator is responsible for the accurate completion of all accounts, communication exchanges and other interactions which occur. The game designer's intentions, both mechanical and substantive, should be carried out. Arbitrary changes by the operator without full knowledge of their implications can do serious damage to the gestalt conveyed. Novice operators unacquainted with the basic communications purposes involved may resort to gimmickry and/or shortcuts to make the game more fun or to establish the game as more relevant to their particular ends. If the audience is captive, this may violate a basic ethic of game use.

It is not uncommon for the operator to intervene arbitrarily, unnecessarily, and with negative results in the human interaction which is taking place in the normal course of a game run. The simplest, most straightforward rule is that the operator should blend into the woodwork at the earliest possible moment and let the game proceed with a minimum of operator intervention. A game is an environment for learning, a communications device designed to establish a vernacular, to permit a particular audience to address a particular problem. The various roles which have been established as part of the game are part of a carefully coordinated system designed to convey a gestalt. An overly strong-willed operator, failing to understand the need to let communication occur spontaneously, can do damage to a game. One factor which an experienced game operator will recognize is the *hubbub factor.* After a certain point of necessary operator intervention, the participants will grasp the ideas and will pursue the problem on their own. The voice level in the room will indicate this point as multilogue ensues.

The operator may also have an obligation to coordinate the game with some larger objective, such as a teaching or public service activity. It is very common among neophyte game operators to use a game as an independent activity, neither preceded nor followed by related material or activities. This may be a violation of the basic communication purpose involved. There are few circumstances where the use of a game is justified as an independent entity. One possible exception is when a game is being run as a demonstration either to illustrate the character of that style of game, or as a demonstration to a group who are reasonably sophisticated about the content and whose primary purpose is to evaluate the potential of the game.

Another area of ethical obligation of the operator to the participant has to do with the presence of "observers" during the course of a game run. Observers can be categorized as casual, interested, or scientific. Casual observers are passersby who want to know a little more about what is happening; they have neither an intense interest in gaming as a technique nor in the subject matter at hand, but simply a general interest in the proceedings. Interested observers are either qualified on the basis of their interest in games or their interest in the subject matter. Scientific observers are there to make observations of player behavior during the game relative to information processing, group dynamics, or other experimental activities.

It is essential to have specific policies for dealing with each of these three types. Casual observers generally are a deterrent to good communication and should be excluded entirely, if feasible. They may be permitted to view the proceedings from an external place. If permitted in the game room, severe constraints should be imposed: absolutely no talking to the operator or any players, no interference with the activities, and a minimum of activity signifying their presence. Interested observers can be included in the run of the game as assistants to the operator. If they are not under the immediate control of the operator, they should be prohibited any communication or exchange with the operator or with the players. The presence of scientific observers raises ethical questions. If there is a scientific experiment underway as a sub-rosa operation in conjunction with the game, prior arrangements must be worked out which ensure that no ethical codes are violated by the experiment or by the presence of the scientific observer.

There is a tendency for observers to become enmeshed in the activities of the game, but in highly tangential and sporadic fashion. The result is that bona fide players, rather than being engaged in multilogue which has been carefully established, are likely to find themselves in a secondary conversation. Since observers are not likely to understand the reasons or to accept these constraints, the best rule is to prohibit them entirely. *Observers in a game are invariably negative factors.*

Designer to Operator. The operator, once the game has become routine, will not usually be the designer and will not have the same information about the construction nor the logic behind the design of the game. Therefore, the designer has a special obligation to provide the operator with information which will allow him to use the game intelligently. This entails an obligation on the part of the designer to provide an accurate portrayal of the game through a variety of devices, in particular the standard description and evaluation form discussed later in this chapter. Also, the concept report or an accurate abstraction of the concept report should be made available to the game operator. Finally, the designer has an obligation to provide the game operator with a game in which all materials are available and are fully operational.

Dissemination of the Finished Game

It is not uncommon to hear the designer of a successful game lament that he has created a Frankenstein and his life is now being consumed by honoring commitments to demonstrate it. This phenomenon results from the noncommercial nature of many of these games and the great difficulty associated with preparing packages of the completed game for distribution to others who have an interest in it. In many instances such dissemination and distribution is a labor of love; it is rarely a profit-making venture. Some designers have transformed a successful game into a product capable of commercial dissemination, and some publishing houses are making efforts to produce good game kits. In any event, the game designer would do well to consider the problem of dissemination at the time that the game itself is designed and particularly during the time of construction. *The successful anticipation of the various aspects of dissemination are directly correlated with the life expectancy of the game designer.*

Packaging the Game

Unless the game is intended for a specific client and a specific use with no intention for further distribution, one of the most immediate considerations is that of portability—the ease of providing a copy of the game to a new user. A second major concern is that of parsimony of expendables and paraphernalia, particularly if the game is intended for frequent use.

In recent years a number of games have been presented to the public in book or monograph form. This has required some cleverness on the part of the designers, but has certainly resulted in a convenient format for both the operator and the participant. Publishers are still uncertain about precisely what combination of materials in book form are both workable and also commercially profitable, but the number of examples now available strongly suggests that within the next few years several successful patterns will emerge.

A variation on this theme is the book or monograph plus a set of paraphernalia. The paraphernalia may be provided as a kit by the publisher of the book or from some secondary source such as the original game designer, the institution at which the game was originally designed, or certain small companies which are beginning to specialize in the provision of kits. Several such companies are doing excellent jobs of preparing and distributing paraphernalia kits which are associated with the standardized books available from commercial publishers. In addition, the books may refer to standard materials available in any city for local purchases, permitting game operators to prepare their own set of paraphernalia.

Many games come as hand-operated and/or computer-operated versions. One of the problems vexing publishers at this time is whether to publish computer programs in full as part of the book form or to make the computer program available through the original designer or the institution which originally provided that game. Since most games are brought up to date as feedback arrives from user groups, the distribution of computer kits must be in a form which is most suitable to the original institution. In any event the distribution of computer programs remains one of the more troublesome aspects of game dissemination, particularly because of the many variations in computer installations. Even installations which appear to be very similar may differ significantly. For this reason it is best to do programming in some basic language such as "Fortran" and require the intended user to make his own conversion. If the game designer feels the material is his own property, he may choose to release only the object deck, which would prevent others from duplicating, modifying, or altering the game itself.

Distributing the Game

Once a game has been completed and is available in kit or book form the problem of distribution still remains. This problem takes two forms: formal and informal. When warranted, it is best to put a game into a formal distribution path at the earliest possible time. This means either an institutional or a commercial setting. Inquiries for the game can then be addressed to the institution or to the commercial firm and the problem of distribution, at least for the game designer, is solved. If this cannot be arranged, informal paths must be maintained. This is generally done by providing the materials to friends and other institutions. In many instances it is necessary to train operators. This may be done either in workshops where intended users are brought to the local institution, or, if the game is a large one, by sending teams to the site where the game is to be used.

Maintaining the Game

Once an operator has gained access to a game and finds it useful, he inevitably encounters certain problems. The first is the replacement of expendable materials used up during the normal course of the game. If the game is copyrighted, an order for materials can probably be placed with the firm that prepared the game. The tendency of users to photocopy materials has two distinct disadvantages: (1) most photocopies are more expensive per unit; and (2) it may be illegal. Therefore, the game designer should consider whether or not expendables are necessary and, if they are, he should explain in the game instructions how they can be replaced. For example, it might be simplest as part of the purchase of the game to give permission to the local user to replace expendables. In some cases it is more efficient in terms of cost and time to have the expendables prepared as a packet by the commercial firm producing the game; in that case, the operator need only place an order from time to time for replacement packets.

A separate consideration is that of the modification and updating of the game. Each use of the game increases the operator's understanding of nuances or changes which might make the game an improved vehicle. Whether or not notions for change originate with the game designer or other users, modification and updating of games is often necessary. The problem then becomes how to transmit these changes to people who are currently using the game. There appears to be no simple answer. The three most useful techniques are: (1) periodic short courses by organizations which design games during which the local repertoire of games is presented and changes indicated; (2) release of published games in modified versions from year to year as use of the game might justify; (3) continued communication by phone, personal contact, or letter between the game operator and the original game designer so that the operator can have access to the most recent version.

Once the game is in use by a variety of operators, relay of feedback to the designer from players is extremely important. Game designers are well advised to prepare a simple one-page pre-addressed form which would permit the participant to make comments about any aspect of the game that might strike his fancy. Another simple expedient for relaying feedback from players is special meetings within the fraternity of game designers at the national and international conventions. Those interested in a particular game can discuss different aspects of the use of the game. This practice has been viable for both the National Gaming Council and the International Simulation and Gaming Association.

Standard Classification of Games

The classification of games for purposes of filing and retrieval should be viewed as an exact parallel to books. Any of the existing classification schemes (for example, the Dewey Decimal or Library of Congress systems) can be employed. At some later time it might be worth the effort, predicated on a much larger population of games, to consider the development of a separate classification scheme for games. For the moment, they should be filed on the basis of content through some system which is known to local users.

Need for Standard Convention in Description and Evaluation of Games

Repeated discussions with those prominent in game design reveals one rather unhappy fact: the only way to understand a game is to actually play it. A crude substitute, only marginally satisfactory, is to call a friend who has competence in the area of gaming and ask him to describe to you the character of the game. This indeed is a very unhappy state of affairs.

It is essential that the gaming profession adopt a standard set of descriptive and evaluative conventions similar in character or purpose to those already used for books. Such a set of conventions must be formulated for games if we are to develop any efficiency in gaining access to game materials short of actually playing the game. *There is a direct correlation between the successful dissemination of the gaming technique and the formulation of interpretive criteria.* (Chapter 8 presents a proposed system of game description and evaluation.)

6 GAME COMPONENTS

There is a logic overriding all serious games which, when carefully stipulated, becomes a useful structure upon which the design of any game might be predicated. Using the word loosely, there is a "grammar" of gaming. This chapter presents the terminology—a standard set of conventions employed in game construction. In one sense this can be viewed as a manual of style, meaning not so much a definitive structure that must be adhered to universally, but rather a convenient set of ideas which might be useful to the game designer. It is to be viewed as a reality which already exists, even if not recognized explicitly by game developers. In the rudest of societies, the very existence of grammar or manuals of style is unknown, yet in their daily lives people follow the basic rules which govern the use of their language.

Some of the materials presented here are predicated on more secure empirical or theoretical evidence than others. Some are simple conjectures based on the observation of the play of many games and will require more careful documentation at a future point. Game components (see Figure 21) are presented under three headings: symbolic structure, game procedure, and scenario. It must be emphasized that these take on

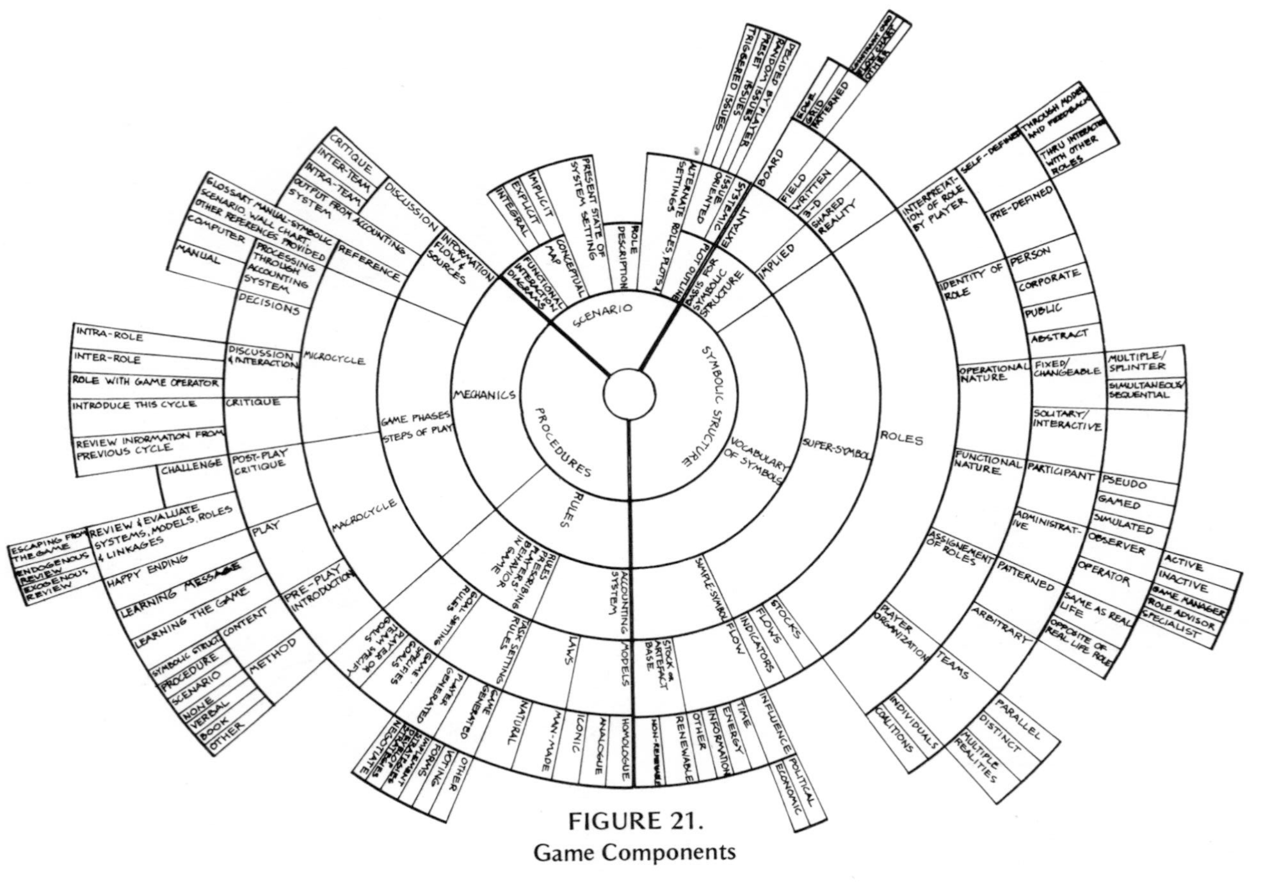

FIGURE 21.
Game Components

their full meaning only in the context of the game design process. Chapter 7, "Repertoire of Techniques," is a logical supplement to the structure presented here in that it intends to provide a range of techniques, a broad heuristic set obtained from the analysis of many games.

SYMBOLIC STRUCTURE

In Section II a language was described as a set of symbols and the rules governing their use. The game has been defined as a communications technology which embodies a game-specific language used in conjunction with one or more conventional languages. These definitions suggest that two levels of skill are required of the game designer; first, the clear articulation of the game-specific language to insure rapid and effective player use; and second, careful integration of this new and unique language with each of the other modes of communication employed in this particular game.

Virtually all game players arrive equipped with spoken and written English and basic mathematics. In many instances, depending on the character of the audience, they may share additional languages including the vernacular associated with a profession or an ethnic origin. Any language known to the participants in advance of the game is defined as "simple" for our purposes. Once present for the game, the players' attentions will be addressed to the new game-specific language and to its supersymbols.

One misuse of a game results from a failure to understand the proper use of supersymbols (that is, new symbolic material). Each time a player enters a new game he is being asked to learn a new "language" for a very specific purpose, and the designer is apt to make one of several mistakes as he introduces this language: (1) the capricious insertion of some new terminology or rule governing the use of that terminology; (2) the failure to include new symbolic material where its initiation would force the player to consider material in a perspective that could not be gained through conventional use; (3) and, most frequently, the presentation of new symbols in quantities far exceeding the capability of humans to quickly assimilate, comprehend, and use effectively. In the final analysis, if gaming simulation is to succeed as a Future's Language, it will be because it does permit the rapid assimilation of new symbols and new structures governing their use.

In summary, *games employ supersymbols, carefully referenced to a conceptual map as a device for conveying gestalt. The number of supersymbols employed is one useful indicator of the nature of a given game. The success of gaming is largely derived from the careful and orderly encoding of information and ideas in supersymbols.*

Through a game we are attempting to find the most efficient communications form to convey a gestalt or permit discussion about a gestalt. We do this by creating a hybrid language form which in part makes use of existing languages, and in part creates a new game-specific language for this particular circumstance. The game-specific language will have three components: the basis for symbolic structure, the vocabulary of symbols, and the rules governing the use of the symbols.

The game construct requires a clear basis for symbolic interpretation. The basis for the interpretation of the symbolic structure employed is either extant or implied. In most cases it is extant, probably because this assists the player in quickly ascertaining the character of the symbols and their use. Extant or visible bases for symbolic structure include boards, fields, and three-dimensional configurations. The great bulk of games employ boards as the basis for interpretation of symbolic structure. In chess, the basis for symbolic interpretation is a board. Given the various pieces of chess but denied the board on which the game is played, the pieces themselves, while symbolic of certain historic figures of power, will be insufficient for actual play of a game because a basic referent set is missing. And so it is with many serious games.

Boards exist in three types: edge, grid, and patterned. The best known of the edge boards is the commercial game Monopoly. A second common board pattern is the grid board. There are many variations on the theme, but basically a grid board has a coordinate system which produces a series of cells that can be identified spatially by referencing the X and Y coordinates. These may be finely grained or quite coarse; they may be sharply and rigidly defined as rectangles or only rough approximations following instead the format or configuration of known land shapes or other basis of reference. The patterned board takes a great variety of shapes. Examples of patterned boards are constraint cards and flow charts. Constraint cards are frequently used in games like *Wff 'n Proof* produced by Layman Allen. A typical constraint card in one of his games has three spaces marked "Permitted," "Forbidden," and "Allowed." The symbols are placed in these three categories according to certain rules. Another type of patterned board is that which employs a flow chart, such as the *Judicial Administration Game* prepared by the University of Southern California, where the player progresses by moving symbols through an existing flow chart. In some instances the players may be permitted to modify the flow chart as the game progresses.

It is necessary to distinguish between the symbols employed in the game-specific language and the symbols employed in the conventional language used in the game. The symbols of the conventional language are called simple symbols. Symbols which require specific definition for use in a game are called supersymbols. In virtually all conventional languages, the rules governing the use of the symbols are defined to permit ready transference to other human beings attempting to learn the language. Rules governing the use of supersymbols are derived from the system being represented.

Supersymbols have never been encountered by the participants of the game before game play. Commonly employed symbols should be avoided if the purpose of the game is to have the players re-examine the function of that particular component. If it is intended that the players pursue the nature of the managerial function in an urban environment, the introduction of the word "mayor" should be avoided. The reason, obviously, is that everyone "knows" what a mayor is. Instead, the game designer might do well to substitute a term which the players will be forced to define; for example spelling mayor backwards as "royam." The interpretation of the meaning of "royam" must be made in the context of the total system being gamed. This is the very essence of games—the establishment of a new vernacular to permit innovative confrontation with reality.

The limits of human beings to absorb new symbolic material is quite constrained. Consider that we expect a child to be at least several years old before he can manage a conventional language in rudimentary form. Or reflect on the amount of time and energy required by an adult to gain proficiency in a foreign language. The game designer should introduce supersymbols with clarity and simplicity. If the variety of supersymbols employed in an artificial systems structure exceeds the ready ability of an adult, it is unlikely that the game will contribute to communication.

Paraphernalia and Visual Aids

Most games employ some type of paraphernalia to symbolize a set of characteristics about a phenomenon associated with the system represented by the game. These materials have no equivalent meaning beyond the game; when they are first encountered by the player their meaning is not understood. However, after the system represented by the game has acquired a greater clarity, these materials gain specific characteristics which in normal game operation are conveyed subliminally. In the latter stages of a game, parallels will be made between game developments represented by this new symbolic material and the equivalent real-world phenomenon. In short, the game creates a jargon with a visual base. The player without being "taught" has learned the jargon and its context of use, and he is capable of using it for sophisticated multilogue with his colleagues. A shorthand has been developed, a game-specific language, which allows not only correlations with present conditions but also speculations about the future. The careful use of supersymbols is important. Abuse through overabundance, lack of clarity, or the failure to replace inappropriate conventional terminology can easily destroy the effectiveness of a game. *One useful indicator of the nature of a given game is a paraphernalia count.*

Roles

The game designer must give careful thought to *role* selection. Material which is being output from other components of the game must be properly directed; conversely, information which is obtained from the role must be processed rationally through the accounting system. The output from all decision points must have a definite target. Roles will generally be limited in number to those most central to the gestalt. Descriptions of roles should be predicated on known real-world counterparts. By deliberately structuring a role so that players are required to deal at a strategic level, or by placing the role under constraints not normally operational in the real world, the occupant of the role can manipulate the system from a new perspective. Most roles are incorporated into a game to permit the participant to experience the system from a context not available to him in the real world.

There are three types of roles: *pseudo-roles, gamed-roles,* and *simulated-roles.* Pseudo-roles are not linked to the basic rule structure; they employ special participants with skills of special relevance to the system under discussion. Pseudo-role decisions are not processed formally through the accounting system, but they may have a real impact on the game. Gamed players, on the other hand, are personally present at the time of the gaming activity, are required to interact with the other players and participate in some stated role, and are required to make decisions which are processed and returned. Simulated-roles are not represented by a human player, but are represented in the mechanics of the game through computer simulation or other forms of operator manipulation. They are used to generate output useful to gamed- or pseudo-roles.

Pseudo-roles are an invention to increase gaminess. They are frequently "on the spot" inventions to assist a human in playing out a part in the communications process which was not provided for in the original design. Game players will frequently invent circumstances which require a response for which no correspondent exists. Pseudo-roles, then, are a tool to be used judiciously by the experienced game operator when their introduction will facilitate communication about the problem at hand. In most instances, the person being asked to fulfill a pseudo-role would not be one of the game participants, but would be an "expert" selected for the occasion.

Simulated-roles, on the other hand, are employed when human behavior is less significant than the generalized response sought from a category of human beings. A good example is the simulation of a given population of households into economic categories. Their economic characteristics might be employed in the game in a variety of ways; for instance, the tendency of a category to secure housing by purchase or rent, patterns of recreation, or other generalized patterns. In such an instance, a simulated-role is more useful than a gamed-role because it successfully avoids the idiosyncratic response of an individual player representing a class of people. Simulated-roles should be used when the response of a broad class or category of people is needed. Gamed-roles, in contrast, should be used when individual response is needed.

The assignment of roles may be arbitrary or patterned. Players may be assigned their own real-life role or a different one. Patterned assignment of roles is warranted only in games of some complexity. Players assigned a gamed-role patterned after their real-life role can be expected to introduce verisimilitude into the game. Conversely, they may be so enamored of the role in its real-world context that they may find it difficult when innovation or new perspectives are suggested. When a player is assigned to a role other than his real-world role, the prospects for dialogue improve markedly and a new perspective is gained.

Players may be organized as individuals, coalitions or teams. *The rule of three argues that single person decision-making should be used sparingly. Preferably, three participants should play the role of an individual* (for example, three participants jointly serving as mayor). The three participants playing the role of an individual may be considered a team, as may several participants working together to perform a function but who have divided the responsibilities. Coalitions may be predetermined by the design of the game. For example, the members of a board of directors may be selected from individuals of various other teams, or coalitions may form of their own volition, depending on the character of the game at hand. Teams may be formed as parallel entities, identical in structure (whether competitive or cooperative), or teams may be distinct groups each charged with a separate function. *The success of a game for gestalt communication purposes is heavily influenced by player organization.*

The identity of a given role may be a person, a corporate structure, a public entity, or some abstract phenomenon. The interpretation of a role by a player may be either predetermined by the designer or self-determined depending on the circumstances. If predetermined, the character of the role should be carefully defined in the concept report and conveyed to the player during the initial stages of game play by written or oral role descriptions. If self-determined, it should be the natural consequence of the participant fulfilling his obligations within the game (contacts with other players as decisions are bargained out or feedback from the basic model). One of the values of self-interpretation of the role is that the players' interactions with the other roles will redefine the perspective of a particular role, and, simultaneously, other roles will be redefined. As a consequence the participants will gain an improved perception of the system.

The roles employed in a game may be either fixed or changeable. Fixed roles mean a predetermined structure to which the player must adhere through the completion of the game. These are more typical of simple games than of complex games. Changeable roles imply those which permit the player (in conjunction with the operator) to alter the basic character of the role as the game progresses. This permits response to increased levels of sophistication of the other players or improved perceptions of the system. Whether fixed or changeable, a role may be structured so that several players are required to participate in it. Conversely, one or more players may be assigned simultaneously to several roles. Splintering of players among several roles is productive when increased communication is sought across lines where it might not normally occur. For example, a player assigned a role in a commercial context might also be assigned a splinter role dealing with the management of some public function.

In the event that splintering of roles is employed, it may be pursued either simultaneously or in sequential fashion. That is, the player, at the outset of the game, may be placed in several roles and given responsibilities associated with each. More probably, a sequential technique will be employed—as the game progresses, the player moves through a series of role assignments.

A role may be entirely solitary or it may be interactive. They are almost universally interactive, but there are situations in which the role should be defined as solitary, pursuing no open dialogue with other roles. Typical examples of solitary roles are roles which serve as arbitrators, judges, or as expert witnesses.

In addition to these roles of an operational nature, there are individuals present during the course of the game associated with the administration of the exercise. These include both operators and observers. From an administrative standpoint, there may be a need for an operator, role adviser(s), bookkeeper, and other specialists. It is always essential to have one clearly defined central figure as the operator of the game whose word is beyond dispute. This does not mean that the operator is not subject to challenge and interrogation by the players during the critiques. Rather, it means that during the normal operation of a cycle the players must submit to the instructions of the operator. Generally, role advisors are used in games which are so complex that the start-up time would be prohibitive without them. Specialists can assist players in learning both the function and the mechanics of the role. Subject matter specialists may be introduced at any time that they aid the operator in transmitting factual information to establish the nature of the system.

GAME PROCEDURES

There has been an undue emphasis on *rules* in gaming simulation, perhaps as a result of the strong heritage of game-theoretic applications. A much more productive concept is "procedures," intended as a flexible term to cover all mechanics of play, including any essential rule structure. Because the game is viewed as an "environment for learning," it is essential that players be able to interact with the game, often in ways not initially perceived by the designer. In so doing, they may feel it necessary to change the structure of the game. Because of game design considerations, certain conditions may be inviolable (for example, the requirement of cycles or iterative experiences; the calculations inherent to a particular model). These may well be called "rules" implying that they cannot be changed. On the contrary, if the players are permitted or encouraged to alter, amend or enrich procedures within the basic gaming structure (for example, moving from a nonexistent definition of acceptable player behavior to an advanced articulation in successive cycles of play), we can maximize learning without the labored and unnecessary specification of an elaborate rule structure.

Rules

Generally, rules as such will play a relatively minor part in a game. Nonetheless, some are inevitable and they must be addressed. They are of two types—those dealing with the accounting system and those proscribing players' behavior during the course of the game.

Virtually all games require a relatively formalized accounting system which deals consistently with decisions made by players. Under such accounting systems there are really three representations: systems of accounts, laws, and models. Systems of accounts become fixed procedural agreements, whether or not known to the players, by which decisions of the players are processed and forwarded to another component of the game. There is an infinite variety of accounting systems existing in the many games available. In some cases, many simple accounting systems are linked together into a totality which is quite complex. Certain natural or man-made laws exist outside of the context of the game but have an application within the game either in conjunction with the accounting system or the models. For example, many games use gravity models, both in an artificial context such as attempts to represent traffic movement, or in a real context such as in attempts to represent the flow of rivers. As such, gravity is a natural law or rule which cannot be violated by players or by game operators. The variety of man-made laws is virtually infinite. If incorporated into a game as a mimic of some known real-world counterpart, man-made laws may be presented as inflexible or subject to change through certain procedural activities established within the framework of the game. Nonetheless, until changed, a man-made law has the same binding effect on player behavior as a natural law.

Within the set of rules of the accounting system are those logical sets which we refer to as models; these may be iconic, analogue, or homologue. Iconic models give the physical appearance of reality, although they need not act like reality. Analogue models are predicated on a logic presuming the parallels of real-world phenomena, and present results which are intended to correspond to the real-world counterpart that they represent. Homologue models (sometimes alluded to as heuristics) present a result which corresponds to the reality we wish to convey, but are predicated on a logic which is in itself not necessarily in correspondence to any known natural or man-made phenomenon.

A second category of rules prescribes player behavior. This may have to do with either task-setting or goal-setting. Goal-setting rules may be prespecified, requiring the player to formulate and specify the goals that he will pursue during the game. A variation on the theme is the presentation of a set of specifications which require that the player or team generate a set of goals and related rules.

The general area of rules prescribing player behavior is typically much less rigid than rules dealing with accounting systems. They will tend to have a degree of latitude either specified or permitted by the operator, or emerge naturally as play progresses. This is equally true of the task-setting rules associated with player behavior; they may be player-generated or game-generated.

In almost all instances, it is necessary to have some game-generated rules governing tasks associated with the routine play of the game. The failure to have such rules results in a chaotic situation and the players will be uncertain about the ground rules. Examples of game-generated rules governing player behavior include the filling out of decision forms, voting, and similar types of phenomena. Player-generated rules appear quite frequently in virtually all games and are to be encouraged because their very formation implies a coherent consolidation of player purposes and objectives. They take an endless variety of forms, simple or complex, fixed or varying from cycle to cycle. Player-generated rules often deal with negotiations between players, teams, coalitions, and/or the game operator. Often it is necessary for the game operator to play the rule of judge in overseeing these rules generated by players. It is a good idea to require that rules be written down.

Mechanics

The mechanics of gaming have a structure which is important in establishing communication within any game. They are subject to modification during a given game as the players create a jargon of their own and as procedures are abbreviated for the mutual convenience of the participants. The following information presents a typical set of mechanics for a given generalized game.

Game Phases

There are two central concepts that must be dealt with by the designer and which must be apparent to the participants: steps of play, and information flows and sources. The various game *phases* referred to as "steps of play" are extremely important to the participant as well as the designer. Games are iterative, meaning that cycle follows cycle and that the happenings within a given cycle repeat and reinforce those which have preceded it. *The success of games in conveying gestalt is largely derived from their iterative nature.* Earlier we spoke of a learning spiral and the need to establish a general level of reference with some logical sense of closure. From this initial point additional detail or information could be assimilated. In a game the frame of reference which establishes a complete cycle and returns it to its closure are the game phases or steps of play. It is crucial, therefore, that players be carefully introduced to the steps of play.

Macro-Cycle. The *macro-cycle* includes the entire set of circumstances from the initiation of play until the conclusion. This includes introduction prior to play, play of the game itself, and the post-play critique. The introduction takes many forms or may be eliminated altogether. It may be an oral presentation or a text presented to players either before or upon their arrival; or it may be a film, videotape, magnetic voice tape, or any other method including simpler introductory games. Preparation time should be as short as humanly possible. The unique character of the game as a communication form requires that the participants' energy be devoted directly to confronting the media. In some contexts, it is quite desirable to have lectures or readings precede the game as preparatory material. It is a mistake to spend long and elaborate introductions to the game itself. The mode requires that the players "take the plunge." Players will inevitably enter a game with a minimum of information; however elaborate introductions are ineffective. A properly designed game will move the player to a full level of complexity through the device of increasingly sophisticated rounds. Keep the introduction brief!

It is usually necessary to give some set of materials to the players so that they will not feel shortchanged. Satisfaction of this psychological need, however, does not necessarily insure ability to use the material intelligently. It is necessary to familiarize participants briefly with the intent of the game, and with the structure, procedures, and scenario. The symbolic structure should be so formulated and presented as to be self-evident to the player. For example, if the game employs a series of wooden blocks each of which has a meaning, these symbols and their definitions should be posted in several obvious places. This is particularly true of those symbolic materials which are visual in nature. The steps of play and a similar list of the macro-cycle activities should be displayed in a prominent place.

Finally, the scenario should be addressed briefly so that the players share some common sense of the problem which they are about to address. In most cases this should be extremely brief (a five-minute introduction or a brief two-page statement). More detail on the scenario may be presented during the initial cycle of play. Initial inertia is reduced if presentation to the players is properly accomplished. *Presentation to players requires a coherent and relatively simple characterization of steps of play, symbolic structure, game mechanics, time scale, information flows, game components, and primary linkages.*

The second phase in the macro-cycle is the actual play of the game. It has three components: learning how to play the game, dealing with the message of the game, and the happy ending.

The first component acknowledges the *initial inertia* which inevitably results when players encounter a game for the first time. During this time the players will feel most distressed and may attempt to escape further participation in the game. One simple technique to overcome this transition period is to walk the players through one complete cycle. Only essential materials should be presented. The participants should be directed through the forms in careful sequence as rapidly as possible so that they can gain a general sense of what is going to happen and can gather some perspective for their own roles, other roles, the various components of the game, and the general gestalt. Each role should address the simplest possible set of materials and decision forms. In later cycles, complexity must be introduced as the players demand it.

The second component of playing the game, usually requiring from three to five cycles, is to confront the conceptual map. This is accomplished by requiring the players to test their understanding of the system. Pulsing is used to generate exogenous problems which create cross pressures. Players are then forced to find solutions. Flying time is jargon for the period during which the players are operating on their own and have moved past the initial inertia. Flying time begins at the time that the hubbub factor first appears, and continues until the participants are ready to engage in sophisticated debate about the content of the game. The operator should be as inconspicuous as possible, administrative procedures should be as smooth as possible, and processing of decisions should be as rapid as possible. Participants are to be left alone until the time of the critique. The only exception to this rule would occur if breakdown of gaming activities were about to take place because of factions or because the decisions went beyond the limits of the technical capability of the game.

The "happy ending" is a final cycle run primarily for the purpose of permitting a player to establish a logical conclusion to his strategies. The operator who arbitrarily stops a game without giving the players some opportunity to conclude their strategies is subject to a fair amount of abuse during critique, and is deserving of it.

The last phase of the macro-cycle is the final critique. It includes escaping from the game, an endogenous review, an exogenous comparison, and a challenge provision. *The hubbub factor, which increases as the game begins to fly, will also fall away as interest wanes. This is the time to introduce the critique.*

Escaping from the game is not to be taken lightly. If the game has been carefully designed, the players will literally be talking a language of their own and will be deeply involved in the game. Escaping from the game requires the players to be given an opportunity to complain about errors, flaws, or unnecessary abuse that they have encountered and, conversely, to glow about their successes. It is essential that they be given a brief opportunity to go through this phase.

The second phase, endogenous review, should be entered by a deliberate announcement that the players are leaving the game and entering into an analytic period. The endogenous review should permit a statement about the systems, models, roles, linkages, scenario and other components of the game, and discussion by the players about the construction of the game, its message, its successes, and its failures. This should generally be brief and somewhat perfunctory since those players who really wish to pursue these questions can be sent the concept report. The availability of the concept report in a well-designed game permits this stage of the critique to go very quickly.

During the course of the endogenous review players must be permitted to challenge any aspect of the game, the system represented by the game, the message transmitted by the game, the models, roles, linkages, manner of presentation, or other aspect of the game, including the use of new symbolic material. Games are typically not constructs of hard science but fairly whimsical and at times fanciful presentations of phenomena. As such, participants may have suggestions which could lead to the replacement of some component of the game and therefore its improvement. The challenge provision ensures that any player who has serious doubts has an opportunity to express his challenge and offer alternatives.

Finally, an exogenous review which focuses the player's attention on the real-world problem should now commence. This review should be permitted as much time as possible. It should be permitted to wind itself down until the group dissolves on its own volition. The purpose of the exogenous review is to capitalize on the vernacular now shared by the entire group in order to concentrate on the real-world problem. This exogenous review should take from 25 to 30 percent of the total time of the game play.

Micro-Cycle. All games consist of a series of cycles, which are iterative and which become more complex cycle by cycle. Within any given *micro-cycle* there is a standard set of phenomena which are confronted by the player.

Each cycle should be started with a mini-critique, the purpose of which is to both review information from previous cycles and to introduce anything unique about the cycle now beginning. Mini-critiques are of particular value if the game is being run on a discontinous mode. They can serve as an opportunity to get the players' thoughts directed once again toward the content of the game. During the mini-critiques, questions about output, decisions or activities which occurred in the previous cycle should be addressed to the satisfaction of the players. This is a good time to introduce the pulse, which focuses the players on some aspect of the game.

Following the mini-critique the next phase of a cycle is discussion and interaction: inter-role, intra-role, and between the roles and the game operator. Intra-role discussion should focus on reviewing the material or output resulting from the last cycle and developing strategies for the cycle at hand. Inter-role discussions should be addressed to seeking information, forming coalitions, developing strategies, and improving communications about the problem. Discussions between the various roles and the game operator may include an individual role, a member of that role or members of various roles simultaneously in discussion with the operator about some problem related to the game for which the operator is serving as expert witness. In some instances, the game operator is obligated to initiate these discussions. Examples include the formation of an ad hoc group to consider some problem, question, fact, or alternative at the request of the operator and to subsequently report to the assembled game participants.

Next in the micro-cycle are decisions which may be of both an inter-team and intra-team nature. The concept report will define the sequence in which these are to be made and give reasons for the sequencing. Generally decisions should be made under time pressure: it is necessary, however, that time pressure here be reasonable.

Finally, the decisions must be processed through an accounting system, whether manual or computer. Regardless of the character of the processing system involved, it is extremely important for the game operator to review the decisions made by the players and to ensure that they represent the actual intention of the player. More importantly, he must check that they do not go beyond the capabilities of the game itself. It serves no purpose for an operator, either through vindictiveness or ignorance, to process a decision knowing that the result will be an embarrassment to the player and an obstruction to progress in the game. Certainly there are many players who would tempt a saint because of their arrogance, ignorance, or plain bull-headedness. Nonetheless, it is a clear violation of operator ethics to process and expose a decision which is patently stupid or irrelevant.

Information Flow and Sources

The game is a device for exploring gestalt. To achieve this, players must be permitted to pursue any angle of the subject from any perspective which seems relevant to them at an appropriate time. They must be provided with both a total systems overview and sufficient detail. For this reason, an essential component of any game is a clearly referenced set of information at both general and detail levels, as well as a carefully articulated information flow procedure. The information provided, in terms of quantity and depth, is dependent on the communication purpose, the sophistication of the players, and the conditions under which the game is normally expected to be played.

Information will generally be in one of three categories: reference materials, output from the accounting system, and information from participants. Reference information will include any relevant material dealing with the subject matter. Standard reference materials should be roughly the same ones the participants would choose if they were to make their own library search for supporting material.

A glossary is an essential item, as it should set forth the game-specific language term by term with a definition as perceived by the designer (or a descriptor to be used in the game requiring precise definition by the players). One value in preparing the glossary is that it serves as an indication of the degree of complexity of the game and, therefore, as an indicator of the amount of energy required on the part of the players to understand the total gestalt.

Virtually all games require a player manual. These may range from a single sheet of rules to a series of volumes for each role. Both extremes are uncommon and probably somewhat ill-advised. The player manual should present, in abstracted form, some of the central questions addressed in the concept report. These would include a statement of the game objectives and the conceptual map, employing flowcharts, tables and overview schematics as appropriate. The player manual should introduce the game-specific symbolic structure, the steps of play, an introductory scenario, and one completed cycle of decision forms. Materials which will be used frequently for reference purposes throughout the game should be included as part of the appendix. These may include maps, data tables, and charts or other graphics that help in maintaining a perspective of the total system.

Other reference materials which can be displayed visually should be provided. In many games, a variety of wall charts need to be posted showing the progress of different variables, cycle to cycle, as they are computed by the accounting system. Any other reference material which will facilitate communication between players should be provided.

The objective of the game is to obtain commitment of the players through specific decisions. The recording of these decisions and the data processing are of little value unless there is a precise, accurate, and rapid response from the accounting system. These results of player decisions become one of the most important sources of information during the game. Players will be frustrated by the failure of the game mechanics to give an accurate and rapid response to their decisions.

The single most important source of information in any game is the discussion inter-team, intra-team, and in a critique with the operator. The values of these discussions cannot be overemphasized for it is through them that much of the information that the player has been exposed to is synthesized.

SCENARIO

The use of scenario parallels its use in a novel or in the performing arts (theater, movies, television). In each case it becomes an integral part of the technique for conveying the "story" or plot. Probably no single failure in game design is more common than an inappropriate use of scenario (too complex or too simple, inappropriate to the audience, unsuccessful timing). Usually this can be traced to either the designer's lack of clear purpose or the operator's insensitive use of the game.

In order to overcome the sequentiality of prose, the author of a novel may introduce the technique of flashback to relate simultaneous events. Each communication mode employs different techniques to convey its story or message and games are no exception. The objective of a game is to explore a complex problem with both a sense of wholeness and detail. The technique employed in gaming is that of the conceptual map. Just as it is difficult for the author of a novel to present simultaneously all of the circumstances which impinge on his story, so it is impossible for the game designer to present the conceptual map instantaneously. For this reason, a variety of devices are employed to work the participant carefully into the mesh of the conceptual map.

The scenario may be presented by text, but more frequently it will be supplemented with various devices to illustrate the present state of the system, including functional interaction diagrams and other graphic materials. Frequently role descriptions will be included for all participants, at least to establish intitial points of reference, and therefore initial points of discussion. Finally, a plot outline will be presented to the player to help him complete his gaming experience. In most instances, the plot will be presented to the players, generally in a series of pulses or as relatively discrete problems which can be perceived in the context of the total system. As the game proceeds these pulses follow one upon the next; and in complex games, several pulses may be initiated simultaneously. Often referred to as "issues," these pulses become tangible handles by which the player can enter into and explore the conceptual map.

Pulses, the systematic presentations of aspects of the total problem, may be either issue-oriented or systemic. If systemic, they are self-generated as the players progress through some scheduled sequence of events which lead them deeper and deeper into the problem. If issue-oriented, the plot may include issues which are randomly presented, triggered by player decision, or pre-set. In the event players are permitted to choose issues, they are required to identify and set them in priority. Random issues represent a set of typical problems that might be productively explored, but their presentation to the players will depend on chance. Triggered issues are precipitated automatically by the accounting system. Pre-set issues have been ordered in advance by the designer to appear during specific cycles.

7 REPERTOIRE OF TECHNIQUES

For the neophyte gamer nothing is more valuable than an understanding of the repertoire of techniques currently in use by the gaming profession. Often a neophyte gamer imitates the style of an established game without being aware of the many different styles available. There is a marked tendency for prominent gamers to have an identifiable style. It is common parlance to identify a game by indicating that it is a typical "Prof. Jones game." Unfortunately, the neophyte is likely to ape the "Prof. Jones" of his acquaintance, but somehow fail to reflect the sensitivity of the master in its new application. The neophyte would do well to master as broad a repertoire of games as possible (see Figure 22).

Unfortunately, it is not simple to become familiar with a broad range of games. The number of available games is in the thousands. How can the neophyte begin to review these materials and capture the essence of the styles and the range of techniques? Studying an encyclopedia of game descriptions will be of limited value because most verbal descriptions do not convey the essence of games well. On the other hand, playing all known games of potential interest is absurdly time-consuming and inefficient.

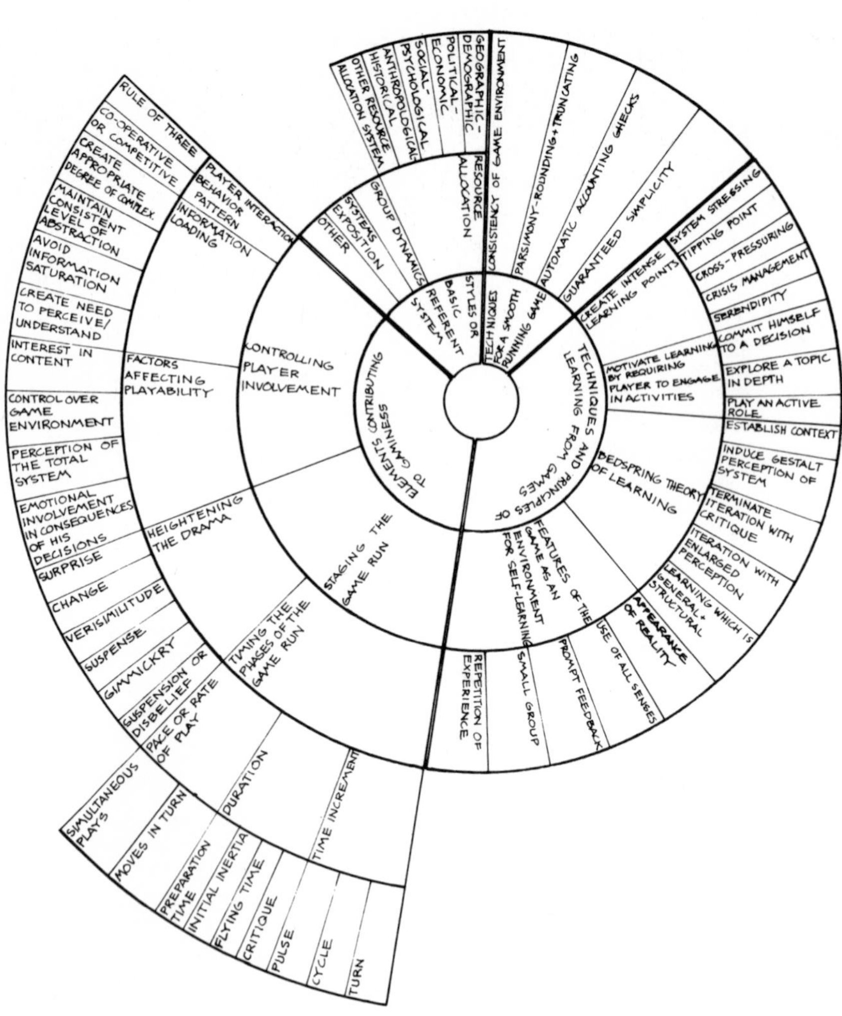

FIGURE 22.
Repertoire of Techniques

Games are often addressed from a subject matter perspective. Various catalogues list games under titles such as military, business, economic, social science, political, urban, and so on. The advantage of such listings is that they lead the searcher fairly directly to the set of gaming materials most closely allied to his interest. It takes very little sophistication about games, however, to realize the inadequacy of such an approach. For example, many frame games are available which do not lend themselves to a subject matter classification. Although a taxonomic structure derived from a subject matter base is not likely to be fruitful, some form of taxonomic structure is essential. The material represented below is a general referent system through which games may be interpreted. It is offered as a perspective through which an observer first viewing a game may draw generalized conclusions about its content, its character, and its possible utility. Most of all, it is hoped that by investigating the characteristics presented below, an observer can increase his knowledge of gaming technique.

BASIC REFERENT SYSTEMS

One key to the essence of a game is the perspective from which it was designed. To know the basic referent system of a game is to know the discipline or set of ideas which shaped the game and influenced design decision. Several games share a group dynamics approach. These present a world in terms of the psychology of human behavior. Other games, by far the majority, assume that most actions can be interpreted as allocation of scarce resources. In any given problem situation, the resources available are inadequate. The problem presented to the players is to find procedures for allocating those resources as well as possible. Resource allocation games may adopt another referent system which becomes the framework within which decisions are made.

For example, *CLUG* uses a geographic framework to illustrate urban dynamics. Resource allocation in the *Inter-*

Nation Simulation occurs within a political framework. An economic referent system provides the basis for *Metropolis.* And the *Marriage Game* treats human relations from a sociological perspective. Other referent systems exist, but most games fall into the resource allocation category. The selection of a given basic referent system may not exclude the use of a particular gaming technique. However, it is generally true that geographic games rely on a board or grid, while social/psychological games do not.

Some games have been spawned by a research team which has resorted to gaming as a way of organizing its perceptions. While group dynamic games inspire human interaction, and resource allocation games develop strategies for alternative deployment of limited resources, these systems exposition games are a tool for exploring complex systems.

The choice of selection of the basic referent system is extremely important because it must be in harmony with the objectives of the client and the characteristics of the participants. If these are properly matched, the task of getting the players quickly into the learning phases will be much simpler than if they are forced into a basic reference system which is alien.

ELEMENTS CONTRIBUTING TO GAMINESS

What constitutes a good game? There is an elusive character which we might call "gaminess" and which is some indication of the players' enthusiasm and willingness to participate. However, gaminess is no accident. For those who are not blessed with an instinctual response, there are some clues which can be relied on during the thoughtful creation and construction of a game.

Controlling Player Involvement

Many players encounter a game without previous gaming experience and therefore feel ill at ease. One way to overcome this discomfort is to require the players to commit themselves right from the inception of the game—the rule of three can speed this process. The rule of three argues that in any given decisionmaking role the highest quality of play will occur if three people are assigned to play the role as though they were one. (Five and seven people together are conceivable, but are increasingly unwieldy.) When three people are assigned to make a joint decision, there is an inherent imbalance which quickly builds the quality of the ensuing discussion. The quality of decisions which result is significantly higher than that achieved by one player making the same decision.

The designer must also consider cooperation, competition, and *cross-pressuring.* Cooperative situations require that the players engage in discussion to solve a mutual problem. In competitive situations, as for example business games, one player's gains may be another's losses; as a result, the participants' behavior varies significantly from cooperative games. By cross-pressuring, we mean placing the player in a situation in which any action produces both positive and negative results. The judicious use of a combination of cooperation, competition, and cross-pressuring can involve players rapidly in game playing.

Once players are involved, if the message of the game is clear, the process of learning takes place automatically and the game operator's role is reduced to that of clerk. Many game operators find it difficult to accept this loss of importance, since they feel more comfortable in the teaching role. In a good game players will explore the system presented on their own volition. They will seek to find answers to questions that they themselves have generated. This means that the operator's role is relatively limited. His main function is to deal with the resolution of technical and mechanical difficulties which inevitably occur.

There is a direct and positive relationship between the success of a game in conveying information and the degree of player involvement achieved. Player involvement can be deliberately manipulated by: rule of three, cooperation/competition, ego threat/ego boost, information loading characteristics, level of abstraction, requirement of commitment, visibility of feedback mechanisms, relevance of substantive content, staging (dramatics, phases, and timing).

Information Loading

Another significant element of gaminess is information loading. During the first cycle of play it is quite common to watch players grow increasingly apprehensive, and, given the opportunity, many will escape at this point. This period is inevitable because a great deal of information is being presented rapidly in an unfamiliar context. To counter this, players should be given no more information than is essential at any given moment. As a game moves through its cycles, each becomes successively more involved and each deals successively with more and more information. As involvement and commitment increase, self-generated need for information increases. Once a player is motivated to raise questions in order to gain the needed information, he is able to assimilate surprisingly large quantities of information. As each cycle passes and the sophistication of the player increases, succeeding rounds become increasingly challenging.

It is also essential that the game maintain a consistent level of abstraction, not only within a given role but between the different roles and components of a game. When one role demands attention to details and another role deals with overview questions of strategy and planning, communication between these players will be minimal. Equally important, the level of abstraction should permit the players to address the questions which are inherent to the objective of the game. Games abound which keep the players so involved in detail that there is no time to think about questions of strategy or to develop heuristics for dealing with real-world problems. Generally, detailed levels of presentation may be useful for elementary training; but if one is dealing with managers or other professionals, the level of abstraction in the game must permit analysis and synthesis of useful heuristics.

Game designers can readily generate greater detail than the average player can possibly assimilate. If the game is constructed with a saturation of information it may be harder to understand than reality. In reality, one at least has the ability to make on-the-spot judgments as to what information to retain and what to avoid. In a game where the context or setting has been made for the player in advance, the player has to assume that the existence of a piece of information implies some necessity for the player to comprehend and deal with it. A possible exception to this is to create situations where the player must choose between channels of information, one of which is productive and the other of which is petty or irrelevant. If this is carefully done, it is possible for the player, after having explored one channel for a short time, to reject it completely and to move on to a second and then possibly a third channel before directing his energies to assimilate the information which has been provided.

Data must be presented in such a way that it will be perceived as information in the context of the game. Games which present page after page of computer output, barely comprehensible to the game designers, are prime suspects. If the variety of materials and paraphernalia is excessive, it may be difficult to create a situation in which information germane to player needs is evident. Many systems, in their real-world context, have voluminous relevant information. Even when these data files are abstracted, they may still represent quantities of information which are very hard to deal with. With adequate resources, it would be possible to present an animated three-dimensional movie, rather than tables of discrete information which would show in a few minutes the significance of this data in overview form.

An important factor contributing to gaminess is the safety of the game environment. The player should be able to make a commitment and to experience the consequences without a loss of face so serious as to carry over into real life. Circumstances must be real enough in the game for a bad decision to be painful and a good decision to be rewarding; it is essential that failures have no ramifications beyond the game.

Commitment on the part of players can be obtained by requiring an explicit decision which is processed through the accounting system and reported back to the player. Even the casual observer can see the anxiety which is generated when a player must first commit his position to paper. At this point, the player becomes involved and wants to know whether his decision was valid. If the game designer has been slipshod, the player is soon likely to find out the error and may justifiably descend on him with vengeance. Although there *are* certain hazards in game design, the exhilaration of jousting with an aroused player (who would be asleep at this point in a lecture) is more than adequate compensation.

If a game is successful, the critique will be a rough-and-tumble session during which people are committed to what they believe. They will pursue with diligence any ambiguities, errors, or undocumented postures which seem invalid to them. Since there is not *one* perspective represented by one player but multiple roles addressing the same problem from different perspectives, a critique can develop exceedingly sharp discussions about the character of a real-world system. A good game will require players to commit themselves to decisions at the earliest possible moment; this process of commitment will grow in complexity and precision as the game progresses.

A good game designer will give careful consideration to the utility of his game as an environment for self-instruction. If the game is so rigid that the player cannot alter characteristics which seem unrealistic, irrelevant, restraining, or which prohibit the player from exploring some alternative future which is of interest, the game has failed since the purpose of gaming is to encourage players to pursue a topic in depth. At the same time, a game provides an environment for the player to confront the total system as a gestalt. A game is also a failure if a player leaves it understanding some aspect well, but having failed to improve his perception of the linkage of this aspect to the totality.

Techniques can be employed to involve the player emotionally in the consequences of the decisions he has made. Various devices, such as the public disclosure of the results of decisions, may evoke a sense of risk on the part of the game player. If a game develops to the point that players are checking off decisions just be "get it over with," the exercise has already lost utility and the critique should be initiated immediately. Another technique which can be employed to maintain player involvement is the use of a roving reporter to reveal players' actions or strategies. It must be emphasized, however, that the objective of the game is to increase dialogue and not to embarrass the players. Successes must be exposed as well as failures. If it seems necessary to reveal a failure, the operator should go to some pains to give the player some way to save face.

Staging the Game Run

There is no doubt that if you were to present a typical participant group with the fact that they were to be the principals in a play that was about to take place without prior training or scripts, you would probably drive most of them away in a panic. Yet this is precisely what the players confront in a game (of course, the operator knows the "play" in advance). The careful staging of the game permits this to be achieved with only one period of anxiety. In any game the first trial cycle inevitably introduces a sense of discomfort (and in some cases mild panic) as the players encounter a complex, foreign environment in which they must commit themselves publicly. The designer can employ a variety of techniques to increase excitement and to maintain player interest.

Devices for Heightening the Drama of the Game

Some devices which can be used to heighten the drama of a game parallel the techniques employed by a playwright. *The suspension of disbelief is essential for player involvement.*

A group of adults gathering to engage in a game will be somewhat apprehensive; and their apprehension will increase as they realize that they will be required to make decisions publicly. Each one will arrive with many considerations on his mind (the morning's news, the latest family agony, and so on). Yet within half-an-hour the same person will become a performer in a play as he suspends disbelief and enters into the scenario!

Drama must never become more important than the original purpose of serving communication. An enthusiastic group of participants is not sufficient evidence of the success of a game; on the other hand, enthusiasm is necessary for success. In order to increase player enthusiasm, surprise and chance may be introduced sparingly in order to model chance occurrences in the real world. For instance, one game uses a throw of the die to determine the granting of federal funds. Verisimilitude, that is, the creation of the appearance of reality from abstraction, is necessary for the suspension of disbelief. Curiously enough, players will ignore great amounts of true to life detail, whereas relatively simple circumstances will sometimes lead the players to accept a game as a substitute for reality.

The period between the time the player has made a decision and the time that the response from that decision has been processed and returned to the player is usually characterized by suspense. This can be used to increase player involvement. Oftentimes when a question before the game must be resolved on an inter-team basis, the period during which the various tems have the matter under consideration will build considerable suspense and the final announcement of its resolution will often result in a spontaneous and marked hubbub. Experienced game operators will recognize that communication following a period of suspense is frequently the time at which the exchange of information is at its peak, fulfilling the communication intent of the game.

Timing: Phasing the Game Run

Games can be fast moving or slow; they can be continuous or broken into distinct phases. Just how the game is phased is partly a question of art and partly a question of skill. In either case it is predicated on the purposes spelled out in the concept report. Virtually all games have time increments: turn, cycle, and phase. Turns are periods of time during which a particular player or players are required to make a decision. Cycles are periods of time during which a series of decisions are made, either simultaneously or sequentially, representing one completed time block—for example, a fiscal year or a month. Phases are combinations of cycles. Typically, there are four phases to a game: the introduction of the game to the players, initial inertia, play of the game, and critique.

Another ingredient in the phasing of a game is the "pulse," which may be generated by the participants or by the operator. The pulse focuses attention on a particular dimension of the system which the players can either pursue or ignore. In a game of any complexity, a variety of information pulses will be simultaneously in play during any given moment of the game. Some of these may be initiated by the operator, some by programmed sequences within the game itself, some triggered by player decisions, or some spontaneously generated. Note that in most media—for example, a lecture—only a single pulse of information will be passed to an audience. In a gaming context, multiple pulses of information dealing with a wide variety of circumstances will be active at any given moment. *Games are successful for conveying gestalt because they employ a deliberate system of informational pulses through an organized gestalt (conceptual map).*

Pace (rate of play) of the game is closely associated with the level of abstraction and the amount of information presented to the player. At the time a game is being designed, an effort may be made to establish the pace at which the game will progress. Unfortunately, the actual pace will probably not be known until the rule of ten is applied. If early trial runs of a game show that it is violating the criteria described in the concept report, review must be undertaken to ascertain if the original criteria or the game should be changed. It is usually best to stay with the original objectives. If the rate of play is too slow, it may be necessary to be harsh in truncating materials or activities associated with the game.

Decision points may be simultaneous or in rotation. If decisions are presented as a series of turns, the situation is more sequential than if simultaneous decisionmaking is employed. Nonetheless, there may be good reasons for sequential decisionmaking—such as having each team focus on the activity of other teams. Unfortunately, sequential decisionmaking is chosen frequently only because it facilitates bookkeeping. Desirable practice is to have play simultaneous, with all teams reaching decisions at the same time. During subsequent cycles, as the players become more proficient with their own decisionmaking process, they become increasingly aware of what other players are doing. This facilitates the conveyance of gestalt about the system. The real world rarely presents us with circumstances in which the players perform in turn, permitting the others to observe. Quite the contrary, things usually happen more or less simultaneously; it is only through a great deal of experience that we gain the "maturity" which permits us to understand complexity.

The duration of a game run is the amount of elapsed time from the onset of the game to the completion of the critique. The game duration should be stipulated in the concept report since it is likely to be influenced by many factors; it must be within the audience constraints.

TECHNIQUES FOR A SMOOTH-RUNNING GAME

The level of complexity of a given game should be a function of the nature of the communications problem being dealt with. Other things being equal, simplicity in all aspects of gaming is to be desired. Remember that you are asking a group of strangers to learn a new language. The more involved the session becomes, the more resistance you will encounter in achieving this goal. To insure simplicity, the player decision form should be distinct from coding forms. If any procedure, accounting activity, rule, paraphernalia, or mechanical aspect of any kind can be eliminated without injury to the game, it should be.

Anger and frustration on the part of players is the inevitable result of operator errors. Such errors can cause the player to lose confidence in the game. Automatic accounting checks should be designed to catch errors before they come to the attention of the player. The operator should be able to recognize at a glance whether responses in a cycle are within the ranges expected. If they exceed or fall below these ranges, the operator should make doubly sure that they are the result of decisions which were intended by the players. If a player commits a gross error (unwittingly leaving a decimal out) the operator should automatically correct this. It is frequently possible to be parsimonious in the accounting procedure. Techniques of rounding, truncating, and approximating are acceptable if they do not alter the significance of the result.

TECHNIQUES AND PRINCIPLES EMPLOYED IN LEARNING THROUGH GAMES

The "art" of gaming, like any art, is probably best learned from experience with the media. Nonetheless, one clue can be offered as to its nature. All games are basically iterative in their structure, reinforcing the hunch that this somehow improves learning potential—this is probably achieved both by successively defining the totality of the problem in increasing detail and by positive reinforcement through repetition.

The earliest literature on gaming viewed it as an exercise in self-instruction, an environment for learning. This environment must have the appearance of reality although the security of the artificial is always present. Players commit themselves, and these decisions receive prompt feedback. The repetition of experience through many cycles of play facilitates learning.

Iterative exposure to a particular gestalt with an increasing amount of detail in each cycle encourages learning which is general and structural. Each iteration should be terminated with a critique which provides the opportunity to address directly things which have been presented obliquely. The iterative progression through cycles helps a player to establish a context which is broad and structural; each additional iteration introduces more detail. It is necessary to require players to engage directly in activities of play, to assume roles, and to commit themselves to decisions. Feedback permits an exploration of a topic in depth; if several players are pursuing a similar pattern simultaneously, the critique offers unusual opportunity for cross-communication.

A variety of techniques may be introduced to facilitate learning: tipping points, crisis management, cross-pressuring, and system stressing. The tipping point is managed by allowing a particular variable to develop along a relatively smooth curve until, at some point either predetermined or resulting from the actions of the players, the variable becomes critical. Perceptive players may anticipate the tipping point and avoid it, or they may fail to agree on a strategy which would prevent the crisis. Crisis management, management by exception, and cross-pressuring are related techniques that can be used to emphasize learning in particular contexts. During crisis management, a situation goes beyond reasonable bounds and the burden of solution is placed on the participants. Management by exception, prompted by information overload or unmanageable complexity, requires that players address their attention only to circumstances critical to management. Cross-pressuring means that a given player at any moment in time will find a set of issues confronting him which contradict another set of issues. As a result, he is forced to rethink the implications of a particular decision stream. Cross-pressuring should be avoided during the early cycles and introduced only progressively during flying time.

System stressing is of particular value as the game is nearing its termination. Once the players have completed enough cycles to feel confident that they know the character of the system and are engaged in sophisticated and continuous dialogue about the problem which is being gamed, a final "test" can be applied by the arbitrary introduction of events which place heavy burdens on some aspect of the system. Players alert to the true character of the system are able to deal with a system-stressing incident with greater facility than neophytes. This technique is usually employed as a last activity in the cycle, immediately before the critique. Players' response to system stressing can be highly innovative and imaginative; in many instances the game will not be designed to accommodate such response and the operator will have to acknowledge this limitation, using the innovative response as a launching pad for the critique itself.

The basis for learning through games will derive from two basic characteristics of games: (1) the game is an environment for self-instruction, permitting N-dimensional entry (and, therefore, simultaneous multiple sensing from different perspectives in a safe environment), and conveying heuristics (general and structural learning) in a responsive environment; and (2) the iterative character of games permits enlarged perception and logical mental closure with each iteration, permitting an emphasis on gestalt or overview, the establishment of context as perceived to be relevant to the player, and reality testing through formal critiques.

8 INTERPRETIVE CRITERIA

Earlier we described a communications continuum and in it referred to a broad variety of communication devices. Even though these vary tremendously in their nature or character, man has developed convenient shortcuts for evaluating their utility in pragmatic day to day situations. The book may be used to illustrate what is meant by "interpretive criteria" (see Figure 23). A typical modern library will have volumes of books numbering in excess of a million; they will range in size from miniatures to portfolio editions and in content they will touch upon virtually every subject of interest to man, through a range of experience that is almost unfathomable. Yet the average citizen can, in a short time, locate the book which is relevant to his interest.

The individual searching for a book, having reached some preliminary notions about the topic, enters the library and goes through a routine search. The search may include seeking information from the librarian, searching catalogue files, reference materials, and similar tools within the library. The searcher will next go to a library shelf where, filed according to some numbering system he will unearth perhaps as many as one hundred books which might be relevant. At this point, if there

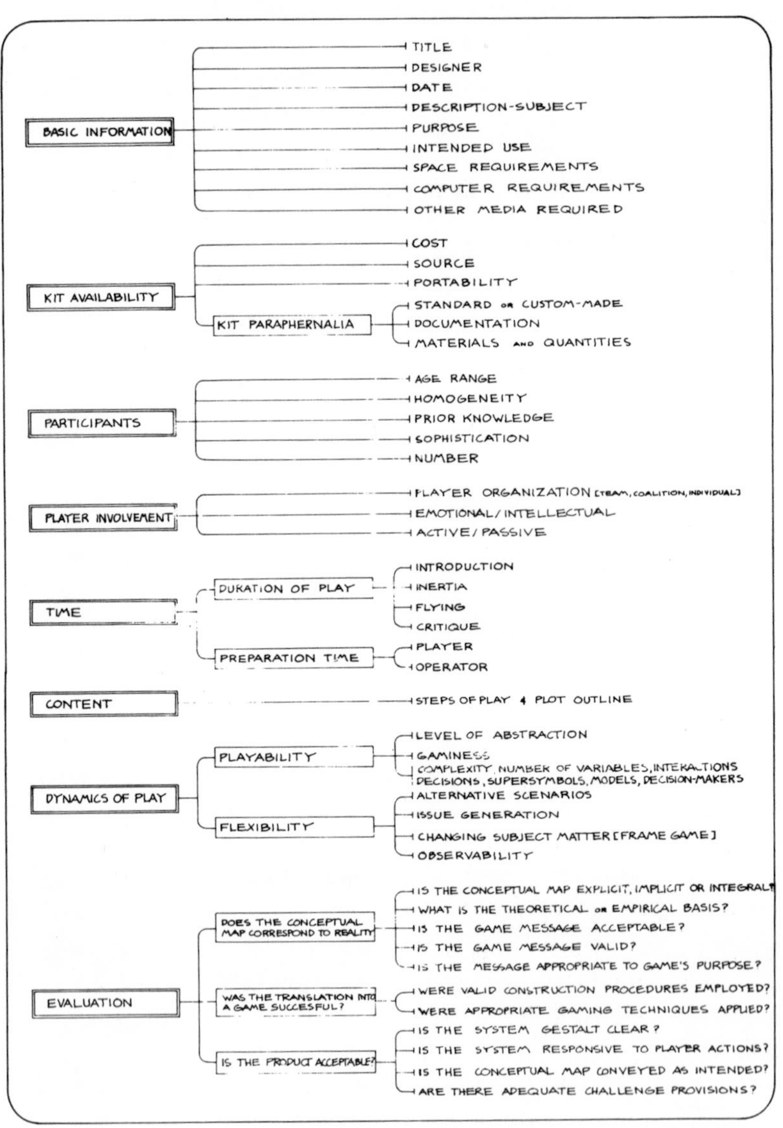

FIGURE 23.
Interpretive Criteria

were no conventions governing the consistent format and presentation of materials contained within books, his task would be exceedingly difficult. The only alternatives available would be to read each document or search out others who had read them. Fortunately, conventions have long been established: books have a cover, title, table of contents, publisher, author, visual identification of size or extent of the material, index, in some cases a flyleaf with brief descriptions, glossaries, appendices, visual materials such as photographs, charts, tables or other introductory information preceding the document itself, introductory and concluding chapters, and the inherent and convenient possibility of flipping through the book rapidly, pausing at various places to gain some sense of the content and therefore its appropriateness.

This standard set of conventions are adhered to with great consistency, and as a result the user is able to select from his initial list perhaps a half dozen books to take from the library for closer examination. In the final analysis, only one or two may be read completely through.

Unfortunately, no such convenient set of conventions is employed by game designers, and so the "game" presents itself to the searcher in an almost infinite variety of patterns. Our salvation to date has been that the library of available games is extremely limited, numbered perhaps in the thousands and thus automatically limiting the extent of the search. The present state of affairs leaves little alternative to the individual seeking to select a game—either he must play the game as a participant or an operator, or he must contact associates who have played it and ask their opinion. Clearly this is an unacceptable pattern. If we persist in failing to develop a set of conventions to which a game designer must adhere, we can expect game selection to remain inefficient. There are several published sources which catalogue available games. These are heroic efforts by the authors to identify, locate, abstract, organize, and present in abbreviated form some statement about the material available. While the efforts are valuable, they fail to fulfill their intended purpose for two reasons:

(1) At some point the volume of games available will defy cataloguing in a single source. As a consequence, catalogues will tend to become more and more specific within the context of subject matter.

(2) Even more important, the criteria currently employed in catalogues is not predicated on any coherent body of theory, and, as a consequence, the brief descriptions are only of modest value. A carefully derived set of conventions, generally agreed upon by those engaged in game design is a necessary precondition to intelligent cataloguing. Interpretive criteria must be developed which are logical, consistent, and predicated on an overall concept of gaming.

Following are eight categories of information which are essential to those seeking information about a game, and which, therefore, should be provided by the game designer for the prospective user. These interpretive criteria might be presented in a consistent format, such as a brief brochure associated with every game.

The eight categories of information are: (1) basic information; (2) kit availability; (3) participant information; (4) player involvement; (5) time considerations; (6) content or subject matter; (7) dynamics of play; and (8) basis for evaluation.

BASIC INFORMATION

Anyone wishing to evaluate a game for its potential use should have available the following basic information:

Title. A brief descriptive title by which the game is popularly known. This will include both any acronym as well as the terminology from which the acronym is derived.

Designer. The name(s) and institution of the individual(s) and client group who are responsible for the development of the concept report and the construction phases of the game.

Date. The month and year in which the game was first released for public use, as well as the date at which this current version was released after modification. It might also be appropriate as a parenthetic note to indicate prior modifications by date if they have been extensive or significant.

Description of subject matter. A brief statement of approximately 250 words which describes the game message. It should essentially be an abstract of the conceptual map represented in the game or an abstract of the conceptual map to be extracted from players.

Purpose. A brief statement of approximately 250 words or less, indicating the communication purpose to be fulfilled by the use of this game.

Intended use. The conditions under which the game is normally expected to be put into play. This would indicate whether it is intended to be used continuously or discontinuously. The context of use should be indicated, such as a public policy session, a citizen participation program, or an academic program.

Space requirements. A brief statement, preferably including sketches, indicating optimal space, both room size and layout, and including the necessary paraphernalia such as blackboards, tables, chairs, and the like.

Computer requirements. First, an indication of whether the game is a hand game, a computer game, or a game that might be run under either mode; second, if the game can only be run under the computer mode, complete specifications of the character of the programming used and the type of equipment for which it is designed. Also included should be the name of an individual or institution from which specific computer information could be derived, including phone number and address to permit convenient access.

Other media required. If any supplementary communication media are required in addition to those provided through the basic kit, they should be listed here with their particular specifications. (For example, videotape equipment, film projectors, and so on.)

KIT AVAILABILITY

Games may never reach the same level of convenient reproduction associated with books. Because games are so specifically tailored to a need and because the industry for their reproduction and distribution is at the moment limited, gaining access to most game kits will remain difficult for some time to come. For this reason, there are several related factors that a potential game user should know.

Cost. This is simply a statement in dollars of the cost of acquisition of the game, followed by information which influences costs such as shipping charges, computer time, replacement of expendables, and fees for assistance and for royalties due to the game designer, if appropriate and demanded.

Source. Specifically, how does one go about obtaining the kit so that the game can be played? What is the name of the individual, the organization, the address, and the telephone number? Is the game available only with initial training or only after some in-service training program? Are there any other constraints that the user should know about which assist him in evaluating the availability of the game?

Portability. Under what circumstances can the game be played? Are any paraphernalia required? Are special requirements such as rooms or special configurations of people required? Are special assistants or computers required? The reader should be able to ascertain just how big a hassle is involved in using this particular game.

Kit paraphernalia. If there is a set of material which is required as a standard part of the game, such as preprinted forms, Lego or wooden blocks, these should be briefly described as an indication of the complexity of the game as well as an indication of the energy required to get the game off the ground. Some games are conveniently packaged into published manuals. The operator and participants are required to remove them from the manual and to maintain them according to certain rules, but other games require that the operator start by a shopping trip to the local five-and-ten-cents store buying sacks of marbles, egg timers, and the like. What paraphernalia required are standard material? What is custom-made? What quantities are required? How are the paraphernalia used? The documentation should, typically, include procedures for management of these paraphernalia during game play. In this instance, some materials are under the control of the operator, some are under the control of the individual teams, and in certain circumstances some may be under the control of an extra player such as a banker. The purpose of the documentation, again, is to permit the intended user to gain some perspective on the degree of hassle associated with the use of the game. Finally, the types of materials and the quantities involved should be stated, whether or not they are standard in a preformed kit or something that must be acquired by the local user.

PARTICIPANT INFORMATION

Any intended user of a game should have a fairly clear knowledge of who the intended audience was at the time of its development.

Age range. What is the age group of which the game is intended? This should be as specific as possible; for example, particular grade in school, undergraduate or graduate student, or age in years. If a broad range of ages are anticipated, as in a public forum, this must be stated.

Homogeneity. The character of the intended audience in terms of their homogeneity or heterogeneity should be established with care. In addition to age which was already discussed, the sex, diversity of interest, geographic diversity, and discipline should be stated.

Prior knowledge. Is it required that the players have prior knowledge of gaming? Are specific warm-up game exercises suggested for lead-ins to this particular exercise?

Sophistication. What level of sophistication is anticipated of the participants with regard to the particular message, conceptual map, or basic problem pursued by this game?

Number. What is the typical number of players expected for inclusion in a normal run of the game? What is the high and low range of participants that can be anticipated? What is the optimal number of participants? If increments of the game can be run or if there are other variations in the game which permit increasing the number of players, give a brief statement about how this can be achieved.

PLAYER INVOLVEMENT

Because of the variety of activities which parade under the title of games, the amount of emotional involvement experienced by participants varies rather considerably from game to game. Some games encourage active emotional involvement, others deliberately orient the participant intellectually. The potential user of a game should have some information available which would give a clue of the designer's intent, including a candid indication of how the game typically comes off during play.

Player organization: team, coalition, or individual. The organization of the participants as individuals, teams, coalitions, or some other structure should be stated. Simply knowing this organizational structure becomes useful to the individual making a critical review of the game. Some statement should be made, preferably through a diagram, about the typical interaction between these players.

Emotional/intellectual. A brief statement should be presented indicating whether the primary objective of the game is to establish an emotional relationship between the players, or whether the primary objective is to establish an intellectual exchange through the jargon of the game.

Active/passive. This means not only the degree of interaction required inter-team or intra-team, but also some indication whether the primary mode of play is thoughtful contemplation or physical activity.

TIME CONSIDERATIONS

Games often take more time than allocated for the run. This implies a poor choice or a careless use of the game. A game which is hurried, particularly at critical times of deep player involvement, cheats the players of some of the advantages of gaming. We must remember that as a communication form gaming is one of the most expensive to develop and use. If the critique, which is the most important single element of a gaming experience, is eliminated, truncated, or emasculated by the escape of fifty percent of the participants, the game itself is inevitably a far less worthwhile experience. No operator should run any game before having experienced it as a player, or at least until careful thought has gone into a walk-through, with the intended group in mind.

Preparation time. The prospective user of a game is entitled to know, in fairly accurate terms, the amount of time required for the participants to prepare for actual play of the game and the amount of time required by the operator to prepare for the run. In addition, the amount of time that the players or participants must spend with the operator in preparation to actual play must be stated.

Time should be allocated to the activities which are required for preparation (for example, readings that are required before participation in the game, warm-up games or exercises, or mechanical activities which might be associated with organizing or preparing for play).

Duration of play. It is convenient to think of each run going through four phases of play: introduction, initial inertia, game play, and critique. It is obligatory for the game designer to include as part of the interpretive criteria a description which will give the intended user an accurate sense of the time associated with each of these phases. If the game can be played with variations—for instance, with different group sizes—then the time requirements should be stated for each recommended variation.

CONTENT OR SUBJECT MATTER

In an earlier chapter we described the conceptual map as an indication of the message that was to be transmitted, extracted, or discussed in a game. It is incumbent on the game designer to provide in convenient form as part of the interpretive criteria a statement of a thousand words or less (roughly equivalent to an abstract) of the game's subject matter. The steps of play of the game should be clearly articulated and a brief outline of the plot should be given.

DYNAMICS OF PLAY

If a hundred games were chosen at random from one of the several available published catalogues, the variations that would be evident in normal play would be extraordinary. Because of this, the intended user needs specific assistance from the game designer in the form of a statement which characterizes the dynamics of play for the game at hand. It is extremely difficult, perhaps impossible, to characterize dynamics of play simply and effectively. Nonetheless, at least two characteristics can be identified and specifications can be prepared which give some inkling of what goes on during the course of play. They come under the heading of playability and flexibility.

Playability. Games range in character from somber to frivolous. In either case, a description of the game ambience would be exceedingly valuable information for a potential user. When discussing playability, the author has the obligation to deal with several types of characteristics. The most significant is the level of abstraction at which the material is presented.

Another characteristic which is more specific in describing dynamics of play is complexity. This entails a specific statement of the number of variables, including their names, description, and purpose; the number of players, models, and data sources; diagrams of player interactions; the basic decision pattern, and the number of decisions required per player per cycle; the complexity of the game-specific language both in terms of symbols employed and the complexity of the basic gestalt being conveyed or considered.

Flexibility. The potential user also has the right to some understanding of the degree of options open to him and the conditions which govern their use. Several specific characteristics should be commented upon. Are alternative scenarios possible? Are they presented? If so, how many and what are their general themes? Is there flexibility in issue generation in this game? Has the game designer provided a variety of issues and are these fixed or flexible? To what extent are they under the control of the operators or players? If they have not been provided as alternatives, what difficulties will be encountered by the operator in generating new ones?

Can this particular game be viewed as a frame game? Is it possible to change the basic subject matter to suit the purposes of the operator? If so, how does one proceed, and what difficulties might be encountered? If change of subject matter is relatively complex, are specific instructions provided somewhere in the basic game kit?

Observability. Does the game lend itself to observation by other than those who are actually participating? Are there specific conditions that should be imposed on observers? Are there specific characteristics to which observers should be directed?

EVALUATION

Gaming is the most specific form of communication available to us and the most expensive. It is therefore incumbent on the game designer to assist the intended user with the process of evaluation of the game. This implies the establishment of criteria that would serve an evaluative purpose. There are three concepts that should be presented as part of the interpretive criteria, and which must, in the final analysis, be answered by the operator or users of the game. The response to each criterion must be in a format appropriate to the game under consideration.

Does the conceptual map correspond with reality? The basic purpose of the game is to present a conceptual map or obtain discussion thereon. Has it been successful? Is there evidence to indicate that the conceptual map has correspondence with reality? Or is it a speculative statement by the designer? If speculative, has it been so identified? When judging this the operator should examine whether the conceptual map is explicit, implicit or integral, and whether it has been an appropriate way to present the material to the players. What is the theoretical and empirical basis for the materials presented in the game? Is it documented, and what is its degree of respectability? Is it basically normative? Is it derived from specific theoretical materials previously established within a profession? Are the data sources known, real, and accurate? Or are they generalizations used in lieu of true empirical data? What is the game message and is it acceptable from the standpoint of the operator/players? Is the message appropriate for the purposes for which the game was employed? Is the message valid?

Has the problem been properly translated into a game? Is the game a successful product in light of its intended purpose? This includes technical questions dealing with the validity of the construction process and procedures employed (the accuracy of the data gathering, computer programming, data reduction, and process of abstraction employed). Were appropriate gaming techniques employed? Were the supersymbols overpowering, confusing, appropriate? Was the level of abstraction appropriate? Were the devices for player involvement sufficient or overdone?

Finally, from the participant's perspective, is the product acceptable? Is the system gestalt clearly conveyed? Has the game and the system represented been responsive to the players' actions? Have they been able to perceive this responsiveness? Are items of detail, viewed as significant by a given player, perceived as having some correlation to the conceptual map? Are adequate challenge provisions provided? Has the critique evoked the type of discussion which would suggest to the players and the operator that they have gained an understanding of the problem at hand, and is that understanding superior to that which they might have gained had they used conventional languages?

A game cannot be evaluated unless its goals have been preestablished; the success of a game can be measured by its ability to convey the conceptual map. Some measures of game quality are: integrity of the accounting system; clarity of information flows; parsimony in data management; consistency of game environment; and increasing complexity from cycle to cycle.

SECTION IV

9 CONCLUSION

At the turn of the century ships at sea communicated brief messages to their land base via carrier pigeon. By Toffler's (1970) reckoning this was in the 799th lifetime. As of this writing, we are entering the 801st lifetime. Carrier pigeons are no longer used as computers, radio, and satellites keep a continuous surveillance of all ships.

Less than a decade hence we confront the "big brother" of Orwell's "1984." The cynic may feel that we do not have a decade to wait. Has man escaped from the slavery of an all consuming ignorance only to enter upon a new era when he is enslaved by technology? Or is there some prospect that his voice can be heard as part of the democratic process?

A recent public hearing was held to obtain citizen input to the General Plan soon to be adopted for a region. Several hundred citizens were present; some were permitted the opportunity to speak for two minutes (by the clock) to their concerns about the plan. There was no acknowledgement, dialogue, or response; all statements were taken under advisement. At a prespecific time the meeting was closed. Those who were denied the two minutes were encouraged to mail in their comments. This farcical event was real. Unfortunately, it is repeated many times daily across the nation as public decision on roads, public buildings, private developments, educational policy, and the like are "brought to the people." We have lost something since the New England town meeting.

There is reason to believe that the coming decades will see crisis upon crisis, shortage upon shortage, with the resultant unstable economic pattern translated into political upheaval in both developed and underdeveloped countries. Problems will be more complex and will be coming up more quickly. More and more people will want to have a voice in the resolution of these problems, and because of the rapid change in many world dimensions there will be a greater urgency for the resolution of these matters.

The solutions offered will be symptomatic but the problems will be systemic. Because of the inherent integrity of complex systems, multiple variables are interwoven into a fabric that is of one piece. But the various projects and programs oriented toward some part or component will frequently fail to take into account the basic nature of the relations.

The last of the states to join the Union is a chain of islands in the Pacific. In terms of geography, climate, societal need, land supply, ad infinitum, Hawaii is quite different from the Mainland. Yet they have constructed an interstate (not intrastate) expressway system to federal standards. Failure to elect this "solution" would have meant loss of the federal money. As a result, scarce land disappears and the automobile is liberated. The great distance between the problem and the bureaucracy which "solves" it results in jarring distortions. Modern circumstances place demands on a representative system that cannot be met by traditional modes of communication.

Complex reality is here and must be dealt with. To the extent that goodwill exists among men, there will always be enormous difficulty in resolving these problems because each man's model of reality differs. We must find new ways to conceptualize complexity, to transmit it to one another, as well as to formulate specific models about future complexity from our known but limited base.

Gaming/simulation is one device that is useful for presenting a dynamic model which is an abstraction of complex reality. Within the context of a game, we develop a highly organized jargon or special language which permits the various respondents to talk to each other with greater clarity than they might do through traditional communication modes. Games can be viewed as abstract symbolic maps of various multidimensional phenomena. As such, they serve as a basic reference or filing system for participants who are concerned with that phenomenon. If these constructs are properly elaborated, they can represent not only a present reality but a future possibility; or more properly, alternative futures.

Everyone at some time or other has wanted a crystal ball to peer into the future. We now need some real-world equivalent. More than ever before, man needs to be able to reminisce about the future, to explore "what if" questions in involved and highly speculative environments. These mythical constructs must be explicit, so that those who have an interest in them can comprehend and, when necessary, challenge the relationship which they represent. If these constructs were built, we would have a model of a future reality which was subject to continuous modification and redefinition, dependent on the best judgment and information of those most likely to be affected.

Man has not one future but many futures to choose from, but this choice is predicated on his ability to articulate the various possibilities before they occur. It is beyond human comprehension to deal with the present in a detailed and factual way, and equally impossible to do so for alternative futures. Instead we need heuristic, overview, or gestalt perception from which we can derive an orientation toward the future that will provide us with crude guidelines for action.

Gaming/simulation is one prospect for assisting us with this task. A game can provide an overview or gestalt perspective, a level of detail appropriate to the task at hand, and mechanisms which illustrate the major dynamics of the linkages among the system components. Gaming has particular potential because it permits the individual to approach complex problems from whatever perspective seems germane and to do so in a context which is coherent and logical, and to experiment in an environment which is basically safe. It permits the individual to gain some sense of how the system responds to his particular proposals.

What are the prospects for this technique in the coming decade? What is the potential role of gaming in the struggle to fulfill human need? Only ten years ago gaming/simulation did not have its present viability; it will soon be ubiquitous. At the present time, games are numbered in the thousands; a decade from now they will be measured in the tens of thousands. As the library of games grows and becomes more sophisticated, the potential for their intelligent use will increase dramatically.

Historically, gaming was a tool of the military copied first by the business schools and then by the social sciences. Only in the past decade has the technique been employed with reasonable success for interdisciplinary research efforts. While the potential of these applications is far from exhausted, the most exciting development to come will be in the area of public policy.

Whenever large numbers of people wish to become involved with complex problems, there is no alternative but to seek new modes of communication. The average human being has the ability to deal with complex phenomena when they are presented in a coherent context. We need not suffer the hazards of depending on an elite unless we are unable to find expedient devices for introducing the citizen to complexity. It is only when we dichotomize, specialize, and truncate that the citizen falls by the wayside. We must rely on the intelligent consensus of a broad citizen base if we are to sustain democracy and if we are to avoid regression to a primitive state where, like the naked ape of the past, our world is controlled by distant and obscure gods, sole masters of the technology that surrounds us. Man must learn to control his destiny. To do so he must manage both uncertainty and complexity.

REFERENCES

MOORE, O. K. and A. R. ANDERSON (1969) "Some principles for the design of clarifying educational environments," pp. 571-613 in David Goslin (ed.) *Handbook of Socialization Theory and Research.* (Chicago: Rand-McNally.)

RHYNE, R. F. (1973) "Communicating Holistic Insights." Fields Within Fields . . . Within Fields 5, 1: 93-104. (New York: World Institute Council)

TOFFLER, A. (1970) *Future Shock.* (New York: Random House.)

APPENDICES

A | SPECIFICATIONS FOR GAME DESIGN

The following list is a series of questions for which parameters must be provided *before* game construction begins. The responses, if carefully delineated, provide detailed specifications at the outset of game construction against which the final product can be evaluated. The questions are arranged in the phases of game design described in Chapter 5.

I. IS GAMING APPROPRIATE?

A. **Define the Problem.** What is the need, condition, or circumstance that prompted consideration of a game? This statement should be brief and convincing to a neutral observer. The problem statement must be sufficiently detailed to permit evaluation of the success of the game when completed.

1. *Client:* Who is the responsible agent? Who is authorized to approve the detailed specifications prior to construction of the game? Who will

evaluate for successful completion? *If no client,* (as when the game is a spontaneous effort by the designer) then an imaginary client should be conjured to insure thoughtful review of the specifications.

2. *Purpose:* What is the primary purpose to be achieved through the game? To transmit information to an audience? To extract information or opinion in questionnaire form from the players? To establish dialogue between players (for example, as a research team)? To motivate players or to prime them for some related experience? To provide an environment in which creative ideas will spontaneously occur? If more than one of these purposes applies, each should be stated explicitly and they should be clearly placed in order of priority.

3. *Subject Matter:* The substantive material which is to be dealt with by the game should be defined as explicitly as possible. If no specific subject matter is implied (for example, frame games like *Policy Negotiations, Nexus,* or *Impasse?*), this should be stated and typical substantive example(s) cited.

4. *Intended Audience:* For whom is the game intended? Will the players be homogeneous or heterogeneous? What age? Sex? Size of group? What is the motivation to participate? If several audience profiles are anticipated, define each category. List in order of priority to indicate which group is prime if design considerations require a tradeoff.

5. *Context of Use:* Under what conditions will the game normally be used? Will it be free-standing or part of a series? Or in conjunction with an

academic course or training program? What follow-up circumstances are anticipated? Will the same group run the same exercise repeatedly?

B. **Practical Constraints.** What mechanical, political, financial, or other considerations are anticipated relative to constraining the use of the product?

1. *Resources:* What financial resources are available for game design, construction, and testing? Is there flexibility to permit alternative designs or cost overruns? How much? Under what circumstances? What financial constraints govern the use of the game? Is the typical cost of play to be within certain limits? What are they? How much time is available for game design? Construction? Testing? Is evidence of productivity to be demanded? At which stages? What evidence? What are the time constraints during the *use* of the game? May it be discontinuous? Will evening or weekend sessions be a normal operational style?

2. *Paraphernalia:* Are any constraints to be imposed on materials used by the game? Must it be portable? Under what conditions? Are storage requirements to be specified? What are they? What demands for reproducibility are to be specified? Must the kit use standardized materials? What are they? Is do-it-yourself reproduction permitted? Required? Are instructions for reproducing the kit to be included?

   May a computer be used? Which one(s)? What programming language(s) are permitted? Required? Must it be batch processed? Run on terminals? Are special peripherals permitted (X-Y plotter, C.R.T.)? What are the limits to computer use in dollars or hours? Per cycle? Per run?

C. **Media Selection.** State the reasons for not using other forms of communication (games are generally the most specific and therefore the most costly media). What are the particular characteristics of the message to be conveyed? May other media be employed with the game? Required? Permitted? Under what constraints (duration, timing, frequency, structured or spontaneous)?

II. DESIGN

A. **Conceptual Map.** What is to be conveyed by this game? Define the system, its components, characteristics, roles, linkages (component to component, role to role, component to role). What considerations are to be emphasized? What themes, issues, or problems are to be stressed?

How is this "message" to be transmitted to the player? Is it to be implicit, buried in the game? Explicit as graphic material or text? Integral in that play of the game requires confrontation with it?

If the message to be transmitted (reality system) is unknown, the purpose of the game being to deduce or extract some perception or reality, system or message, in what format should the game produce it? Only as a perception retained by the players? As a written record through text and graphics (player generated)? As a physical representation (iconic model) created by the players? What roles govern the retention, release, or transmission to sponsor results of play?

B. **Gaming Considerations.** Gaming is characterized by an incredibly diverse set of techniques. Which of these are desirable? Required? Prohibited? Are parallels with particular existing games sought? Which ones? Any to be omitted? Why have they been rejected?

1. *Repertoire:* What style of game is sought? Emphasis on group dynamics? Or more intellectualized emphasis? Should allocation of scarce resources be central? Or is emphasis to be placed on formulating or conveying a system's gestalt? What basic style or character is desired?

   Is the material (message, conceptual map) to be expressed from a particular orientation (field or discipline; for example, psychology, geography, and the like) implying both the perspective and jargon?

   What level of abstraction is desired? Geographic or social scale? What time frame or horizon? What scale of reduction in time? How are power or finances to be conveyed?

   Are game management constraints to be specified? Operator skill, quantity, or training? What level and style of protocols and administrative forms are desired?

   How are players to be organized? By group? Individually? Are coalitions to be permitted? Encouraged? Are multiple roles for one player appropriate?

   Are particular analogies to be encouraged or omitted by the designer (some known system or concept)?

   What structure is to be incorporated for issue generation within game play? Are they to be predetermined or player generated? Random or preset? Linked? Under what conditions?

Is a physical board to be used? Are constraints of size or complexity required?

2. *Art:* "Gaminess" in the final analysis will depend on the skill of the designer. Some considerations, however, may be specified by the client which limit or direct this somewhat elusive characteristic. What degree of player involvement is desired? Large emotional content or emphasis? Or a more deliberate or intellectualized character? Ideally periods of intense involvement will be interspersed with more detached or analytic sessions.

   How is the game to be staged? Are particular room arrangements or player configurations to be specified? Are constraints to be placed on pre-game activity? Are warm up exercises to be considered? Under what conditions are critiques to be held? What duration? Is the style to be free (a "happening") or more controlled?

   Are particular learning principles to be emphasized? Is an iterative approach required? How many cycles minimum? Are they to grow more complex? Can level of complexity be stipulated or guided?

   Games are best perceived as environments for self instruction. Are players to have complete freedom of movement within the game or is it to be guided? By the designer? By the operator? By the conscious choice of the players? Are the players to be permitted to invent their own rules? May they alter game procedures? Under what circumstance and frequency?

3. *Design Principles:* Several elements of design are common to all (or most) games, it may be desirable to specify conditions or characteristics of some of these as design requirements. Is a

scenario to be specified? Are alternative scenarios desired? Is the scenario to be explicit, detailed? Highly abstract? Mimickry of some existing source document? Is it to be capable of modification by the players? The operator? How many resources (time, money) may be permitted for modification during a typical use of the game?

A game is a communication mode which employs its own distinct "language," and, therefore, each game requires a unique symbolic structure. The character of this structure should be specified. Is it to be physical? Three-dimensional? Should its complexity be restricted to permit being learned in a specified time by new players? Are symbols to be of a commercial source (such as Lego)? Are they to be presented initially in a codified form? A glossary? A visual aid for continuous display during play? Is a board to be employed? A map or other visual(s)? What degree of complexity is permitted (quantity of new symbols employed, visual details of maps or boards)? Are there any constraints or requirements as to conventional languages or media to be employed (math, statistics, Fortran, flow charting)?

The character and utility of games are heavily influenced by the rules and procedures they employ. These may be very rigid (as in games of logic); procedural in that they are specified as requirements to orderly play (as in most social science games); or only partially existent (as in situations mimicking a social dynamic) where players are encouraged to develop their own, or to modify a starting set. What is the character sought in this game? Are circumstances governing the basic accounting system to be treated differently from rules governing player behavior? Is the accounting system to be expressed in a computer language? If not, may it be so complex as to require a calculator? How much operator training is necessary for use? How much time is required for routine processing?

Basic complexity of play of any given game is probably best revealed by inspecting the list of "steps of play." Are these, or any subset, to be pre-specified (for example, "prepare a budget," or "make written estimate of consequence of . . . before viewing next output," and so on)? How lengthy or involved is this to be? Can the desired effect be described as advice to the designer? How are they to be presented to the players? Initially? Each cycle?

What information flows are to be provided for? Denied? Emphasized? (Player to player, player to component, component to component.) Are they to be monitored, recorded? Under what circumstances? By whom? Are they to be preserved beyond the game?

What time scale is to be employed? How is the game to be paced? What duration to a cycle? A game? Is timing to be truncated with successive cycles?

C. **Concept Report.** Games are notoriously hard to evaluate. This can be improved upon if a concept report is required of the designer *prior* to game construction. This report should be a synthesis of those considerations reviewed under the preceding sections "Is the Game Appropriate?" and "Design." It should be a statement of the reality to be conveyed or objectives to be achieved through the game. Is the concept report to be reviewed? By whom? What time intervals for review? What procedures apply to resolve disputes? Is the final product to conform to the concept report? What latitude of difference is acceptable? What penalty(s) apply in case of failure? Is construction to begin before the detailed concept report is approved by the sponsor?

III. CONSTRUCTION

If the concept report is carefully prepared and reviewed, construction should be routine and uneventful. However, if the project is large, some particulars may be pre-specified by the client.

A. **Pre-Player Activities.** Are project management procedures to be specified? Are reports to be prepared which document the various components of the game? If so, how will they be circulated? Must there be client approval? Most games deal with systems that are complex and nonlinear; yet game processing is usually rigidly sequential because of mechanical constraints. The order of processing of various models, components or decisions must in some sense be artificial. Is it to be pre-specified to the designer? In games of any complexity, there are numerous components (roles, models or simulations, paraphernalia, accounting systems, and so on) which must be separately designed and/or constructed. These are then assembled and tested. Usually many modifications are necessary to bring a good game together, often necessitating compromise with original specifications or objectives. Are such changes to be reported to the client? Is the concept report to be altered to reflect them? Is approval required? Is data collection, reduction, and loading subject to any quality constraints? Which data items? What degree of accuracy during the assembly and linkage? The entire model must be calibrated to reflect accurate response. Fudge factors (arbitrary values to scale some component up or down) are often used to correct errors. Are those to be reported and appended?

B. **Testing the Game with Players.** Most games cannot be claimed as valid unless they have met the "rule of ten"—that is, at least ten "live" games, the last three of which required no changes (other than perhaps cosmetic or superficial adjustments). Is the game to be tested? With what conditions? Are written evaluations to be required of players? Is the game to be demonstrated for the client?

IV. USE

The game, when, complete, is no longer the responsibility of the designer; however, certain considerations incidental to use may be pre-specified.

A. **Dissemination.**

1. *Ethics:* Is the product to be private property (client's or designer's?) or in the public domain? What are the designer's obligations to the sponsor, to users? If private property, who holds the copyright or patents if any? Are royalties to be paid?

   What user-related ethics must be considered? Is the design nonmanipulative? Is related literature accurate in describing the game objective and particulars? Are certain debriefing considerations to be mandatory for player protection? Is the game to be used in some larger training context? Are "demonstration" runs potentially a waste of player time in which they must be appraised?

2. *Mechanics:* What requirements are to be established for packaging, distribution and operator training? Is the game to be modified and updated? How will these changes be released? Who will distribute the game? Are fees or charges to be permitted for game materials? Are these to be limited to a particular dollar amount? Are they to be waived for certain users? Is the client entitled to multiple sets? How many?

B. **Interpretive Criteria.** Games, unlike other media (books, films), are very difficult to judge unless they are actually played. While this may be an inherent difficulty, some steps can be taken to lessen the problem for perspective users.

Is a classification number of some type to be assigned and included in the documentation (for example, Dewey Decimal or Library of Congress)? Is a description to be included integrally in the kit which addresses the major points under the preceding section "Is Gaming Appropriate?" or is an abstraction of the concept report required? Is this to be pretested with potential users and reevaluated after they have used the game to insure accuracy and clarity?

C. **Evaluation.** Is the designer-builder required to initiate a formal evaluation of the utility of the product? Is validity to be measured against the reality it purports to address? Against the independent judgment of professionals who know the intended context of use? Against the independent judgment of professional gamers? Against the reaction of players? Other criteria? All of the above? If the game is found wanting, what procedures apply for its modification?

To conclude, these notions are intended to suggest a reasonably comprehensive set of questions a client (and/or designer) may wish to specify before a game is commissioned. Since each game is to fill a specific need, these can only be used to prompt a careful search of conditions appropriate in the particular context.

B CONCEPTUAL MAPPING

The illustration entitled "Gaming 1973" (Figure 24) was prepared as a "conceptual map" for conveying information to a potential group of gamers, national and international, who were being invited to attend the first joint meeting of the National Gaming Council and the International Simulation and Games Association. Its purpose was to illustrate the breadth of material to be covered at the convention and to illustrate the type and organization of subject matter which was anticipated at the various conference sessions. Clearly a standard format or outline form could have been employed to achieve the same purpose. Nonetheless, this example illustrates the ability of a conceptual map to attract the interest or attention of the reader, and to present a rather complex statement about an anticipated event. (Another example of a conceptual map is shown in Figure 20.) This section presents two techniques that might be employed to develop a conceptual map.

FLIP CHARTING

In this instance, it is assumed the game to be developed reflects some complex reality, or substitute for a

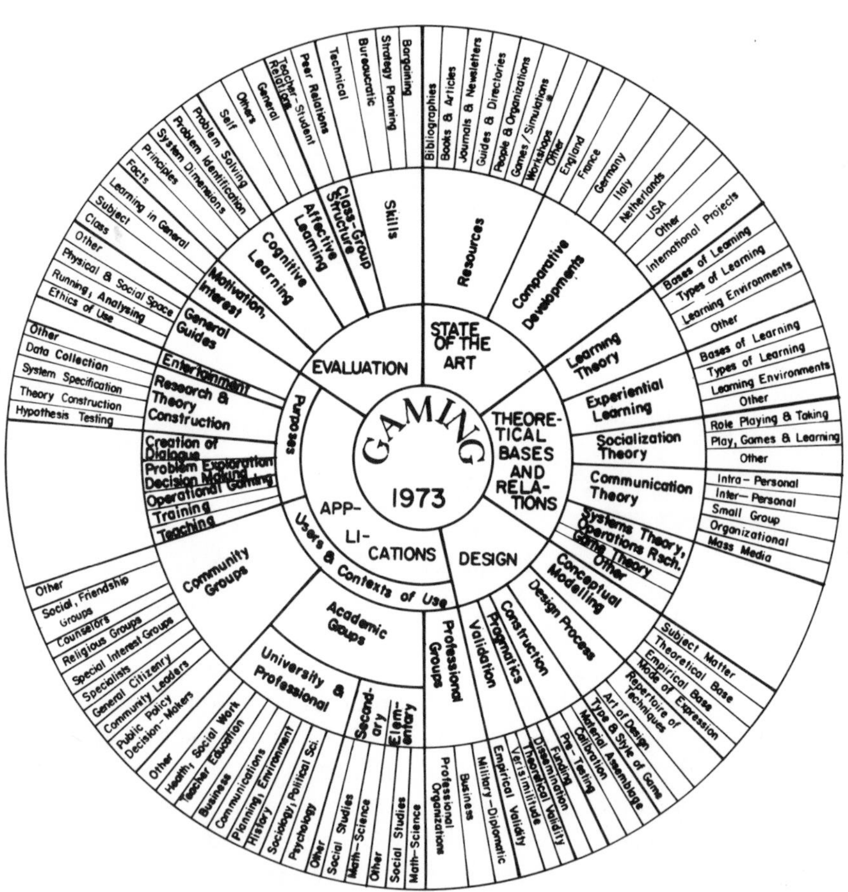

SOURCE: Cathy S. Greenblat, format adapted from Richard D. Duke (prepared for the 1973 joint meeting of the National Gaming Council and the International Simulation and Gaming Association, Gaithersburg, Md.).

FIGURE 24.
Gaming 1973

complex reality, which is to be abstracted for later player manipulation in game format. It is further assumed that the perception of the reality being sought does not reside comfortably in the head of the designer, but rather that the designer seeks expert assistance in its formulation. The objective, then, is to find an efficient, straightforward procedure which will not inhibit the various assembled experts, and which will encourage them to commit themselves to their perceptions in crude written schematic form from their own perspective and with their own jargon. Finally, it is assumed that when the process is completed that the game designer will study the product and abstract from it a single coherent statement which is subsequently circulated among those previously assembled for their confirmation or objections. In those many instances where interdisciplinary teams must work jointly, procedure of this kind is mandatory.

The first step is to assemble a small group (five to nine persons) who meet the following requirements, either individually or collectively:

1. A discussion leader who has skills in small group activity, and an awareness of conceptual mapping (both in terms of its objectives and in the particulars of the technique).
2. A series of separate specialists whose subject matter orientation and prior experience gives them a pragmatic orientation vis-a-vis the reality being pursued.
3. A series of subject matter specialists whose training and inclination is more theoretical.
4. An individual who, previously oriented to the undertaking, will serve as a committed devil's advocate in a disinterested manner. That is, his function should be to pursue with diligent questioning the presentation being made by any individual, so that the jargon or perspective of the presenting individual is forced into an explicit and understandable mode. The devil's advocate should be disinterested in the sense that he should have no commitment to the particular subject matter; no axe to grind in the final product.

This group should be transported to a secluded location where the necessary amenities and creature comforts are provided, and where the intensity of the sessions will not be disrupted by spurious, arbitrary, incidental, or random events. These arrangements must be known to the group prior to such an undertaking and the arrangements must be acceptable to them.

Adequate facilities must be arranged to ensure the success of the procedure. A comfortable room is a prerequisite. An announced, but inconspicuous, and nonstop tape recording should be arranged for all the intensive sessions—this will permit the game designer to rerun the sessions and clarify points which have been addressed several times during the course of the flip charting procedure as the perspectives of participants change. *Most importantly,* centrally located to the group must be a large flip chart with gridded paper and an array of pencils, pens and similar paraphernalia. The basic rule is that the assembled group must stay in an informal semicircle confronting the flip chart. When speaking, an individual must stand by the flip chart with some instrument of writing in his hand. Any individual may start a fresh page at any point the mood strikes. No pages may be removed from the flip chart under any circumstances, nor may their order be altered in any way. The development of ideas becomes a series of vignettes which are expressed graphically at different points in time and from the perspective of different speakers. They form, in very crude fashion, a sequential conceptual map. The final product would be far too unwieldy to transmit ideas to any fresh group. However, it is beneficial to the participants as the meetings progress. The players flip backward and forward to the hieroglyphics on the flip chart, illustrating linkages or correlations between ideas expressed at different times by different individuals.

It is essential that a schedule be established at the outset. Typically, three sessions a day of two or three hours each is appropriate. It is essential that these be interspersed with free time during which the participants may pursue their own interests. All participants should be given a carefully developed packet of material prior to their arrival which describes the subject matter and the basic objectives of the game. Such material should be neutral as much as possible (selected articles might be obtained from several sources reflecting different viewpoints or evidence from a study or studies might be presented without comment).

The sessions themselves must be allowed to emerge as happenings around a central theme. The discussion leader must be aware of the theme for that session and must gently but consistently bring the participants back within its general dimensions. It is important, however, that the individuals be permitted to speak to that theme from any perspective no matter how disconnected or unclear it may appear to the discussion leader or the other members. It is the job of the devil's advocate to make each individual be more lucid in conveying the ideas or concerns which have been brought up. The objective is to establish an imagery of the total system as perceived by the group. Specific effort must be made to identify the major components (decisionmakers or logical units which function as decisionmakers) and the linkages in the system which seem to have particular significance. For this reason, a separate theme should be elaborated at the initiation of each session.

When comment from individuals seems to be at odds with earlier comments from the same individual, this should be noted by the discussion leader and during a lull in the session the discrepancy should be introduced. Discussion of these discrepancies often reveals a basic lack of knowledge or lack of communication about the system.

Finally, it must be observed that such an undertaking is extremely demanding of the participants. The discussion leader must be prepared to end a given session abruptly should it become disorganized or should the group wind down to a nonproductive state indicated by iterative comment, hostility, or disinterest.

The flip charting procedure has been used in a variety of circumstances with good results. Its final success will depend upon the leader abstracting the sessions into a carefully prepared concept report. In fairness, this concept report must be circulated to all the participants.

BASS-ACKWARD ANALYSIS

This very simple methodology, surely employed by others under a different name, can be extremely effective as a device for organizing complexity and permitting its abstraction to a level that facilitates game design.

Initially, there is a stage of muddling-about where the objective is the formulation of a problem statement which is acceptable to the client. This will be an iterative process as different perceptions of the problems emerge. The second stage is to assemble all known segments of information, data, bits of theory, descriptions, linkages, roles, or any other component or piece of information which seems relevant to any of the participants. These are to be randomly collected without concern for their coherence or with any initial evaluation of their final utility. Each of these assembled ideas or problem descriptors is to be placed on a separate three-by-five card, with a brief description. These cards are then sorted into piles of clustering ideas according to any logic which seems to be defensible at the moment. This is an iterative process and the logic for the sorting will have to be defended repeatedly.

On some appropriate space, preferably a large wall with a tackboard surface, the clusters of descriptors are arranged in temporary fashion, group by group, as seems appropriate. In the initial stages, the clusters will be quite small, consisting of only three to five descriptors which are logically related. As the process progresses, the clusters will become increasingly larger.

In the next phase, the display area is organized conceptually as a wheel that represents a totality into which all of the clusters must logically be inserted. This inherently forces the squeezing of some ideas into lesser significance and the inevitable discovery of gaps. As individual clusters are formed into sectors, argument will develop about the appropriateness of a given descriptor-set.

The process described is iterative, and should continue until the group performing the task is satisfied that the two-dimensional wheel is an accurate reflection of their perception of the reality being abstracted. Having achieved this organization of gestalt, the task becomes more difficult. It is now necessary to look for a conceptual explanation which accurately explains the phenomenon. When this emerges, it can be tested by the introduction of a variety of hypotheses. These must be carefully related to the entire configuration in order to establish that an internal consistency exists.

Finally, the entire configuration should be committed to a more convenient format (such as a chart), and the necessary abstractions, omissions, and redefinitions undertaken as may be required.

C | LIST OF GAMES CITED

AT-ISSUE!

R. D. Duke and C. S. Greenblat

"Regional Planning of Monterey Bay—A Triology of Issue Oriented Games for Citizen Use." Final project report prepared for the Council of Monterey Bay.

The Environmental Simulation Laboratory
University of Michigan
Ann Arbor, Mich. 48104
(December 1973)

CLUG - Community Land Use Game

Allan G. Feldt

The Free Press
Riverside, N. J. 08075
(© 1966)

CONCEPTUAL MAPPING . . .

R. D. Duke and C. S. Greenblat

Radius International, Inc.
321 Parklake
Ann Arbor, Mich. 48103
(1973)

FUTURE

Olaf Helmer, T. J. Gordon, Hans Goldschmidt

Institute for the Future
Riverview Center
Middletown, Conn. 06457
(© 1966)

IMPASSE?

R. D. Duke and C. S. Greenblat

Radius International, Inc.
321 Parklake
Ann Arbor, Mich. 48103
(1973)

THE INTER-NATION SIMULATION

Harold Guetzkow and Cleo H. Cherryholmes

Science Research Associates, Inc.
259 East Erie Street
Chicago, Ill. 60611
(© 1966)

JUDICIAL ADMINISTRATION GAME

Richard McGinty et al., Comex Project

University of Southern California
Los Angeles, Calif. 90007
(1973)

THE MARRIAGE GAME

Cathy Greenblat, Peter J. Stein, Norman F. Washburne

Random House
201 E. 50th Street
New York, N. Y. 10022
(© 1974)

METRO–APEX

Richard D. Duke et al.

The Environmental Simulation Laboratory
University of Michigan
Ann Arbor, Mich. 48104
(1967)

Manuals available from:

ERIC Document Reproduction Service
Leasco Information Products, Inc.
P. O. Drawer 0
Bethesda, Md. 20014

METROPOLIS

Richard D. Duke

Radius International, Inc.
321 Parklake
Ann Arbor, Mich. 48103
(1969)

MONOPOLY

Charles W. Darrow

Parker Brothers, Inc.
190 Bridge Street
Salem, Mass. 01970
(© 1935)

NEXUS

R. H. R. Armstrong and Margaret Hobson

Institute for Local Government Studies
University of Bermingham
P. O. Box 363
Birmingham B15 2TT, England
(© 1970)

POLICY NEGOTIATIONS

Frederick L. Goodman

School of Education
University of Michigan
Ann Arbor, Mich. 48104
(© 1974)

SNAFOR

William Bentley, Stewart Marquis et al.

School of Natural Resources
University of Michigan
Ann Arbor, Mich. 48104
(1973)

SQUARE MILE

Milton Bradley Company
Springfield, Mass.
(© 1962)

WALRUS - Water and Land Resource Utilization Simulation

Allan G. Feldt and David Moses

Sea Grant Advisory Services
University of Michigan
1101 N. University
Ann Arbor, Mich. 48104
(May 1972)

WFF 'N PROOF: THE GAME OF MODERN LOGIC

Layman E. Allen

1111 Maple Avenue
Turtle Creek, Penn. 15145
(© 1962)

D GLOSSARY

TERM	*DEFINITION*
ACCOUNTING SYSTEM	The formal representation of the game model including any models, simulations, heuristic devices or conventional accounting procedures.
BARRIERS	Impediments to a clear interpretation of reality; barriers of language, knowledge, prejudice, human limitations, and so on.
BASIC REFERENT SYSTEM	Internalized heuristics for structuring interpretation of complex reality.
CHALLENGE PROVISION	Allows player to challenge any portion of the game as designed. If the challenge is acceptable, the game will be modified accordingly.

COMMUNICATION, GESTALT	(see GESTALT COMMUNICATION)
COMMUNICATION, SEQUENTIAL	(see SEQUENTIAL COMMUNICATION)
COMMUNICATION MODE	A form of communication composed of a language, a pattern of interaction, and a communication technology.
COMMUNICATION TECHNOLOGY	Device for encoding, transmitting, and decoding a message.
COMPLEX REALITY	Complex, interactive, and/or dynamic system, either abstract or concrete.
CONCEPT REPORT	A written statement of the conceptual map and the procedure for transforming it into a game.
CONCEPTUAL MAP	Internalized, organized gestalt comprehension of complex reality.
CRITIQUE	Discussion between players and operator about the game run; entails discussion not only about the run itself but also about the real-world analogue.
CROSS-PRESSURING	Places the player in a situation such that any of several available decisions will have negative impact on his position.
CYCLE, MACRO-	(see MACRO-CYCLE)
CYCLE, MICRO-	(see MICRO-CYCLE)
DIALOGUE	Interrupted serial message alternating in direction.

FRAME GAME	A game whose procedures are consistent from run to run, but into which new content, subject matter and data can be loaded and calibrated for a new purpose each time it is played.
GAME-SPECIFIC LANGUAGE	A symbol set and its conventions of use, unique to a given game.
GAMED-ROLE	Individual present in the game with his decisions processed by the game accounting system.
GAMINESS	A quality of liveliness that makes a game enjoyable to players.
GAMING/SIMULATION	A gestalt communication mode which contains a game-specific language, appropriate communication technologies, and the multilogue interaction pattern.
GESTALT	A structure or configuration of physical, biological, or psychological phenomena so integrated as to constitute a functional unit with properties not derivable from its parts in summation. *(Webster's Third New International Dictionary)*
GESTALT COMMUNICATION	A communication mode capable of conveying gestalt.
HUBBUB FACTOR	The change in noise level discernable when players engage in multilogue.
INITIAL INERTIA	The initial difficulty in getting players involved in a game.

INTERNAL REPORT	Report on game design decisions intended only for design team use.
INTERPRETIVE CRITERIA	Criteria which can be used to interpret or better understand games such as methods of classification, description or evaluation.
LANGUAGE	A set of symbols and the conventions governing their use.
LANGUAGE, GAME-SPECIFIC	(see GAME-SPECIFIC LANGUAGE)
LEVEL OF ABSTRACTION	The degree of correlation between reality and the model employed in the game both in terms of the extent of the structure and the level of detail.
LINKAGES	The relationships which are specifically established within the accounting system.
MACRO-CYCLE	A complete run through all four game phases.
MICRO-CYCLE	A complete iteration through the game processes: review of last processing, multilogue, decision, processing of decisions.
MULTILOGUE	Multiple, simultaneous dialogue organized by a pulse.
PATTERN OF INTERACTION	The relationship between parties engaged in communication.
PERCEIVED REALITY	Impressions of reality as obtained through barriers.

PHASE	One of the periods during a game event: (1) introduction; (2) initial inertia; (3) playing the game; (4) postplay critique.
PROCEDURES	Those actions incumbent on the players and operators to ensure successful completion of the game.
PSEUDO-ROLE	Individual present in the game with his decisions not processed by the accounting system.
PULSE	A problem, issue, alternative, or information presented to the players through the game used to trigger an exchange of messages between players.
REALITY, COMPLEX	(see COMPLEX REALITY)
REALITY, PERCEIVED	(see PERCEIVED REALITY)
REPORT, CONCEPT	(see CONCEPT REPORT)
REPORT, INTERNAL	(see INTERNAL REPORT)
ROLE	Character assigned to someone with prescribed pattern of behavior.
ROLE, GAMED-	(see GAMED-ROLE)
ROLE, PSEUDO-	(see PSEUDO-ROLE)
ROLE, SIMULATED-	(see SIMULATED-ROLE)
RULES	Actions or behavior incumbent on players, operator, and accounting system which cannot be altered.

SCENARIO	Plot outline and setting of game.
SEQUENTIAL COMMUNICATION	Communication dependent on the sequential presentation of ideas.
SIMULATED-ROLE	Individual not present in the game, but role simulated by the accounting system.
SUPERSYMBOL	Any symbol whose meaning is specifically defined for the game.
SYMBOLIC STRUCTURE	The contrived symbolism employed in a game.
SYSTEM, ACCOUNTING	(see ACCOUNTING SYSTEM)
SYSTEM, BASIC REFERENT	(see BASIC REFERENT SYSTEM)

E | GAMING – THE CONCEPTUAL MAP

On the following pages a diagram is reproduced in six parts. These can be removed from the book, cut out, and taped together to form a wheel which presents many variables associated with the initiation, design, construction and use of gaming/simulations.

A single sheet, 30" diameter version of this diagram suitable for posting can be obtained from:

Radius International
321 Parklake Avenue
Ann Arbor, Michigan, 48103

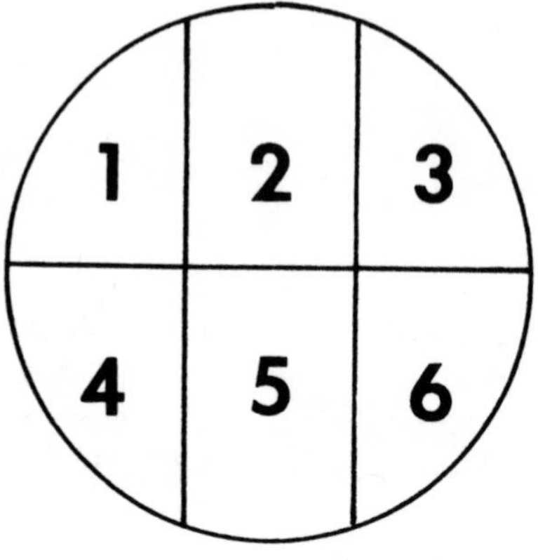
1
2
3
4
5
6

1

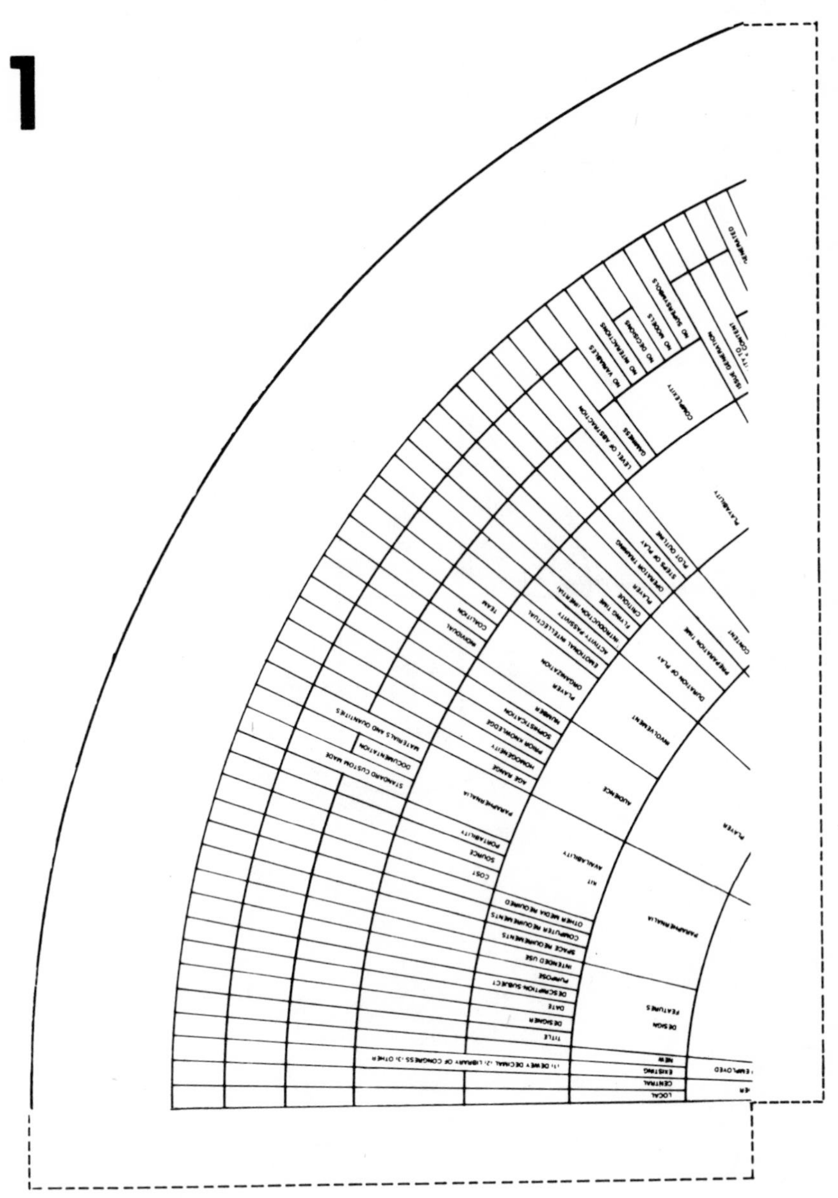
LOCAL
CENTRAL
EXISTING
NEW
(1) DEWEY DECIMAL (2) LIBRARY OF CONGRESS (3) OTHER
TITLE
DESIGNER
DATE
DESCRIPTION SUBJECT
PURPOSE
INTENDED USE
SPACE REQUIREMENTS
COMPUTER REQUIREMENTS
OTHER MEDIA REQUIRED
COST
SOURCE
PORTABILITY
PARAPHERNALIA
STANDARD CUSTOM MADE
DOCUMENTATION
MATERIALS AND QUANTITIES
AGE RANGE
HOMOGENEITY
PRIOR KNOWLEDGE
SOPHISTICATION
NUMBER
PLAYER ORGANIZATION
INDIVIDUAL
COALITION
TEAM
DESIGN FEATURES
PARAPHERNALIA
KIT AVAILABILITY
AUDIENCE
INVOLVEMENT
PLAYER
DURATION OF PLAY
PREPARATION TIME
CONTENT
PLAYABILITY
COMPLEXITY
LEVEL OF ABSTRACTION
GAMINESS

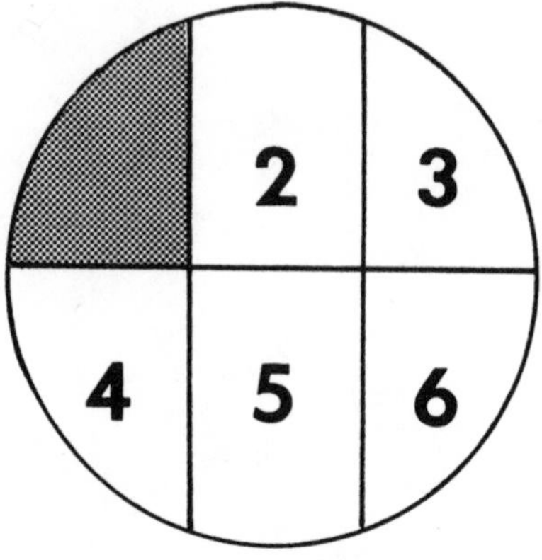
2
3
4
5
6

2

GAMING
RICHARD D. DUKE
USE
INTERPRETIVE
CRITERIA
DESCRIPTIVE
CLASSIFICATION
INITIATION
DEFINE THE PROBLEM
MEDIA SELECTION
PRAGMATICS
CONCEPTUAL MAP
REPERTOIRE OF TECHNIQUES
ART
TECHNIQUE
GAMINESS
STYLE
EVALUATIVE
CONCEPTUAL MAP
WAS THE TRANSLATION PROCEDURE APPROPRIATE?
IS THE PRODUCT ACCEPTABLE?
WHAT IS THE FORM?
WHAT IS ITS PEDIGREE?
IS THE MESSAGE ACCEPTABLE?
WERE VALID CONSTRUCTION PROCEDURES EMPLOYED?
WERE VALID CONSIDERATIONS GAMING CONSIDERATIONS APPLIED?
WERE APPROPRIATE GAMING CONSIDERATIONS APPLIED?
IS THE SYSTEM GESTALT CLEAR?
IS THE SYSTEM RESPONSIVE TO PLAYER ACTIONS?
IS THE CONCEPTUAL MAP CONVEYED AS INTENDED?
ARE THERE ADEQUATE CHALLENGE PROVISIONS?
IMPLICIT
EXPLICIT
INTEGRAL
THEORETICAL
EMPIRICAL
IS IT VALID?
IS IT APPROPRIATE?
IS YOUR RESPONSE OBJECTIVE?
IS YOUR RESPONSE SUBJECTIVE?
TIME
DYNAMICS OF PLAY
FLEXIBILITY
OBSERVABILITY
ALTERNATIVE SCENARIOS
DESIGNER
PLAYER GENERATED
OPERATOR GENERATED
CLIENT
PURPOSE
SUBJECT
AUDIENCE
USE
MESSAGE CHARACTERISTICS
MEDIA
RESOURCES
PARAPHERNALIA
DEVELOPMENT
USE
(1) REAL (2) HYPOTHESIZED
DIALOG
PROJECT
EXTRACT
(1) AGE (2) SOPHISTICATION (3) HOMOGENEITY
CONTEXT OF USE
DISSEMINATION
(1) QUALITATIVE QUANTITATIVE PRECISION (2) SUBTLETY AMBIGUITY INTANGIBILITY
(3) TIME CONSTRAINED PERMANENCE (4) SEQUENTIAL GESTALT ANALOGY COMPLEXITY
TYPES
CHARACTERISTICS
COST
TIME
(1) COMPUTER (2) MATERIAL
CREATION
EXPRESSION
(1) EXPLICIT (2) IMPLICIT (3) INTEGRAL
EXPERT — EXPERT (RESEARCH)
PROFESSIONAL — LAYMAN (e.g. PUBLIC POLICY)
EDUCATION (CONCEPT)
TRAINING (SKILL)
SYSTEMS CONCEPTS
OPINION
(1) TEACH (2) MOTIVATE
(1) THEORY GENERATION (2) HYPOTHESIS TESTING
(1) PRO CON (2) DELPHI PREDICTION (3) CONCEPTUAL MAPPING
ISOLATED
INTEGRATED
INTEGRATED
ADVANCED
PRIMITIVE
(1) SEQUENTIAL — GESTALT (2) SPECIFICITY — UNIVERSALITY
(4) CONVENTIONS EMPLOYED (5) CODING — DECODING
CONSTRUCTION
USE
DEVELOPMENTAL
RUNNING
SIMULATED
REAL
(1) WRITTEN (2) EMOTIONAL (3) TECHNICAL
(1) INFORMAL (2) FORMAL
(1) MULTI-MEDIA (2) HYBRID
EMPIRICAL
THEORY
TEXT
GRAPHICS

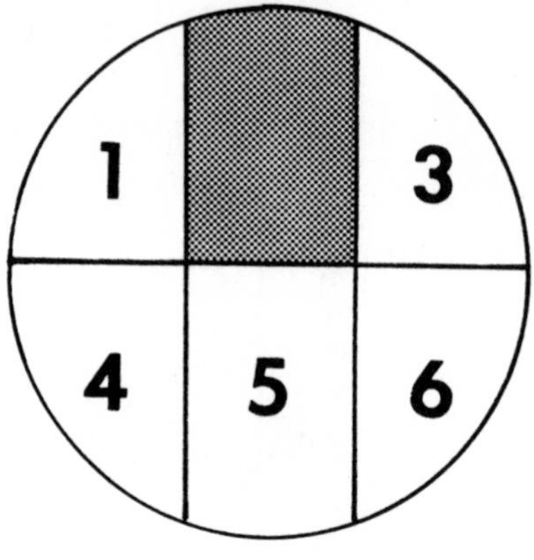
1
3
4
5
6

3

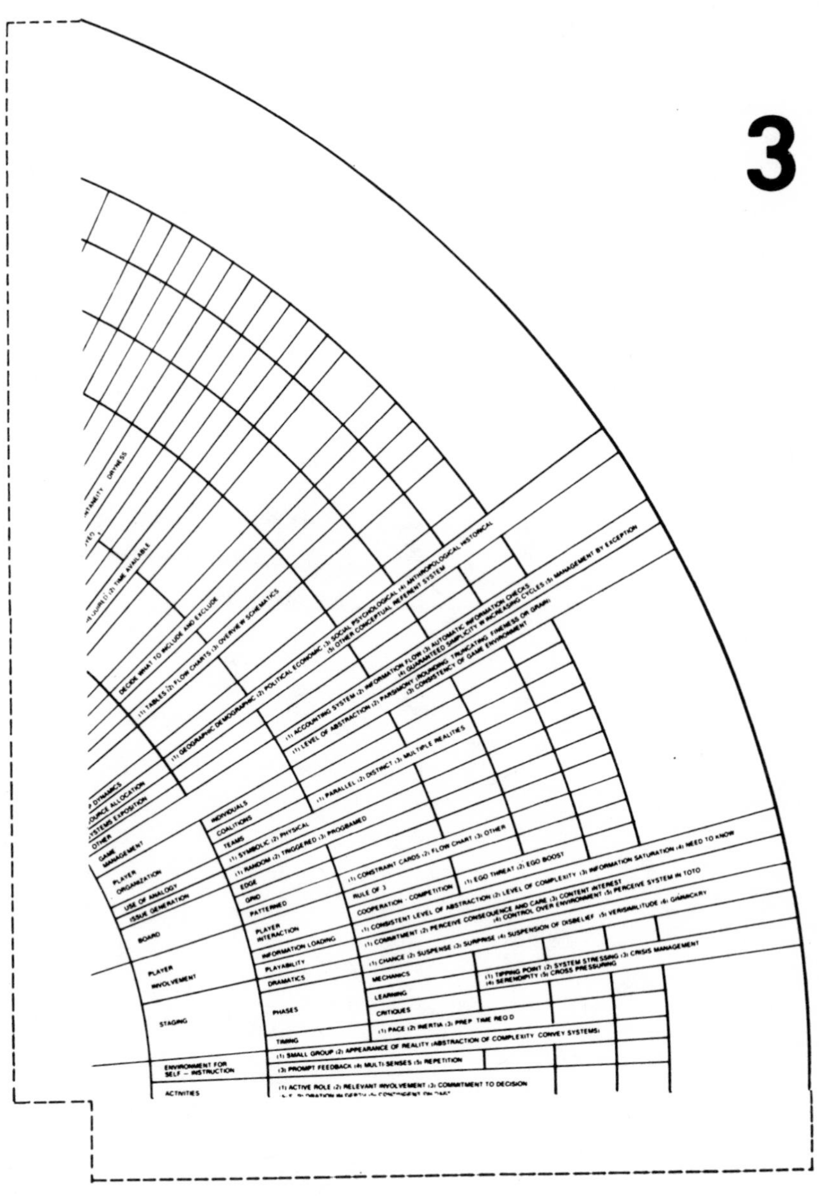
(2) TIME AVAILABLE
DECIDE WHAT TO INCLUDE AND EXCLUDE
(1) TABLES (2) FLOW CHARTS (3) OVERVIEW SCHEMATICS
(1) GEOGRAPHIC DEMOGRAPHIC (2) POLITICAL ECONOMIC (3) SOCIAL PSYCHOLOGICAL (4) ANTHROPOLOGICAL HISTORICAL
(5) OTHER CONCEPTUAL REFERENT SYSTEM
(1) ACCOUNTING SYSTEM (2) INFORMATION FLOW (3) AUTOMATIC INFORMATION CHECKS
(4) GUARANTEED SIMPLICITY W INCREASING CYCLES (5) MANAGEMENT BY EXCEPTION
(1) LEVEL OF ABSTRACTION (2) PARSIMONY (ROUNDING TRUNCATING FINENESS OR GRAIN)
(3) CONSISTENCY OF GAME ENVIRONMENT
(1) PARALLEL (2) DISTINCT (3) MULTIPLE REALITIES
OTHER
GAME MANAGEMENT
PLAYER ORGANIZATION
USE OF ANALOGY
ISSUE GENERATION
INDIVIDUALS
COALITIONS
TEAMS
(1) SYMBOLIC (2) PHYSICAL
(1) RANDOM (2) TRIGGERED (3) PROGRAMED
EDGE
GRID
PATTERNED
(1) CONSTRAINT CARDS (2) FLOW CHART (3) OTHER
RULE OF 3
COOPERATION - COMPETITION
(1) EGO THREAT (2) EGO BOOST
BOARD
PLAYER INTERACTION
INFORMATION LOADING
PLAYABILITY
DRAMATICS
(1) CONSISTENT LEVEL OF ABSTRACTION (2) LEVEL OF COMPLEXITY (3) INFORMATION SATURATION (4) NEED TO KNOW
(1) COMMITMENT (2) PERCEIVE CONSEQUENCE AND CARE (3) CONTENT INTEREST
(4) CONTROL OVER ENVIRONMENT (5) PERCEIVE SYSTEM IN TOTO
(1) CHANCE (2) SUSPENSE (3) SURPRISE (4) SUSPENSION OF DISBELIEF (5) VERISIMILITUDE (6) GIMMICKRY
PLAYER INVOLVEMENT
STAGING
PHASES
TIMING
MECHANICS
LEARNING
CRITIQUES
(1) TIPPING POINT (2) SYSTEM STRESSING (3) CRISIS MANAGEMENT
(4) SERENDIPITY (5) CROSS PRESSURING
(1) PACE (2) INERTIA (3) PREP TIME REQ D
ENVIRONMENT FOR SELF — INSTRUCTION
(1) SMALL GROUP (2) APPEARANCE OF REALITY (ABSTRACTION OF COMPLEXITY CONVEY SYSTEMS)
(3) PROMPT FEEDBACK (4) MULTI-SENSES (5) REPETITION
ACTIVITIES
(1) ACTIVE ROLE (2) RELEVANT INVOLVEMENT (3) COMMITMENT TO DECISION

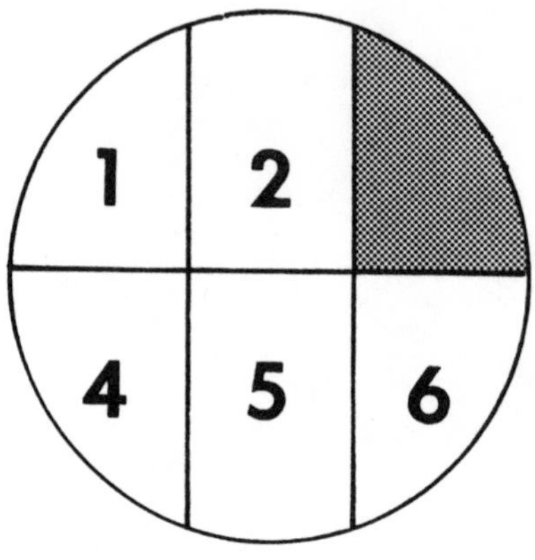
1
2
4
5
6

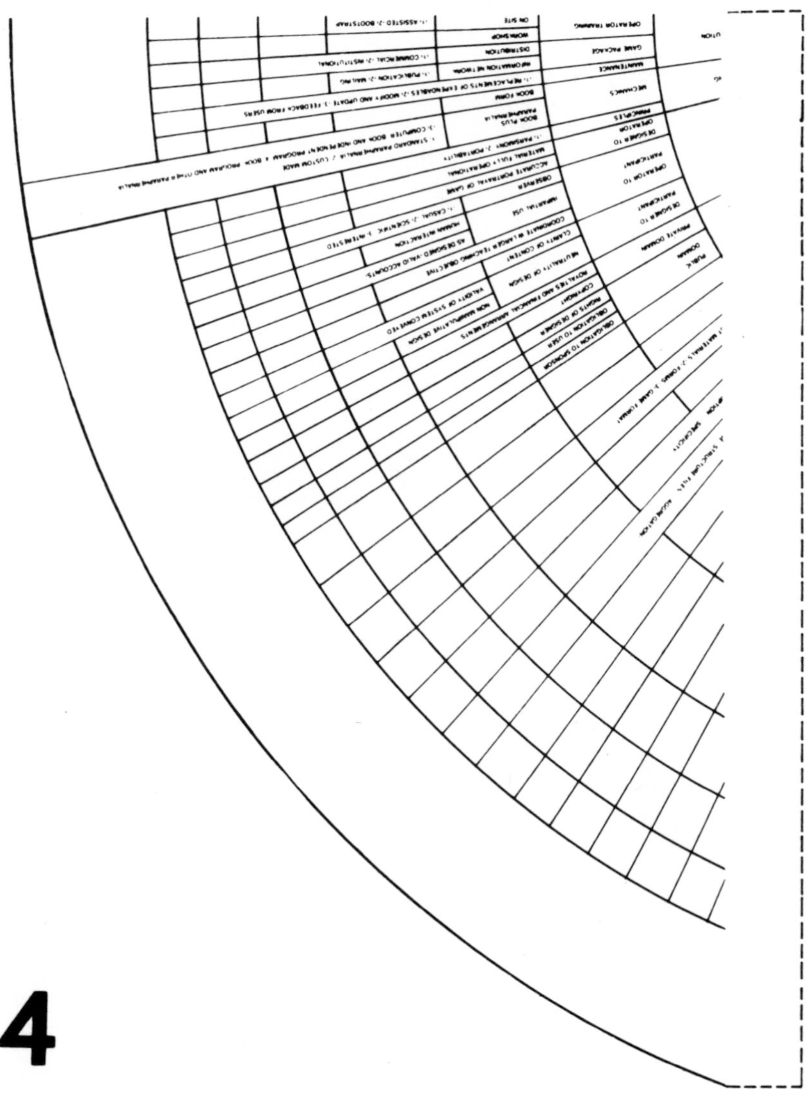

4

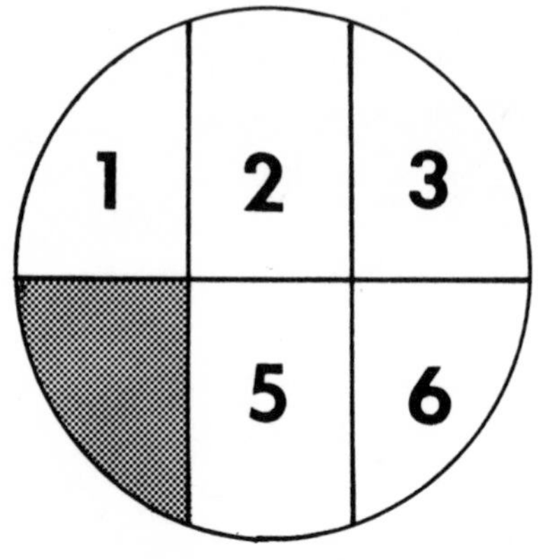
1
2
3
5
6

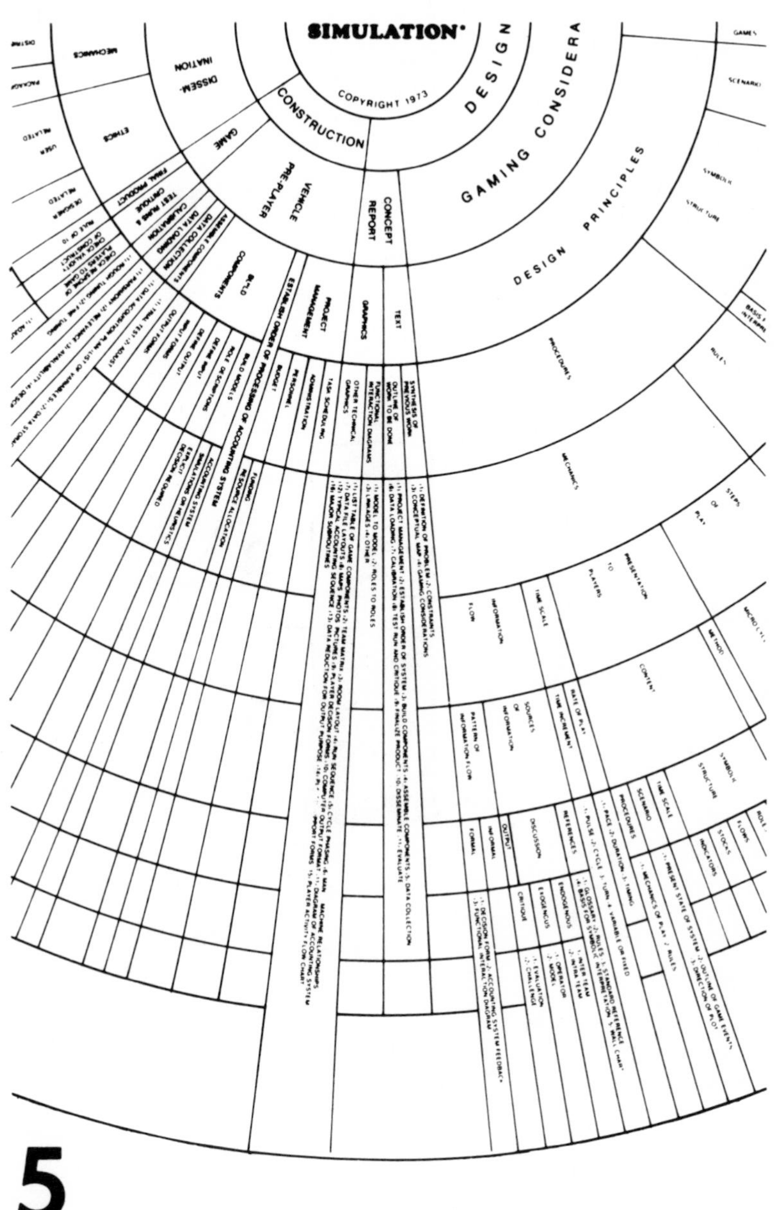
SIMULATION
COPYRIGHT 1973
DESIGN
CONSTRUCTION
GAMING CONSIDERA
GAMING PRINCIPLES
DESIGN PRINCIPLES
CONCEPT REPORT
PRE-PLAYER
VEHICLE
GAME
DISSEM-INATION
MECHANICS
ETHICS
BUILD COMPONENTS
PROJECT MANAGEMENT
GRAPHICS
TEXT
ESTABLISH ORDER OF PROCESSING OF ACCOUNTING SYSTEM
RESOURCE ALLOCATION
PROCEDURES
MECHANICS
PRESENTATION TO PLAYERS
CONTENT

5

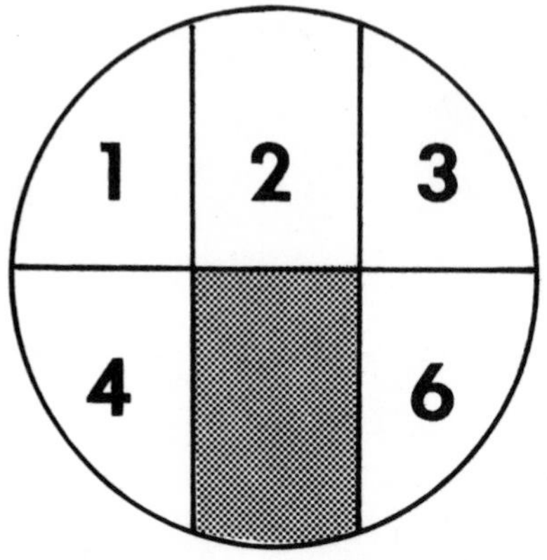
1
2
3
4
6

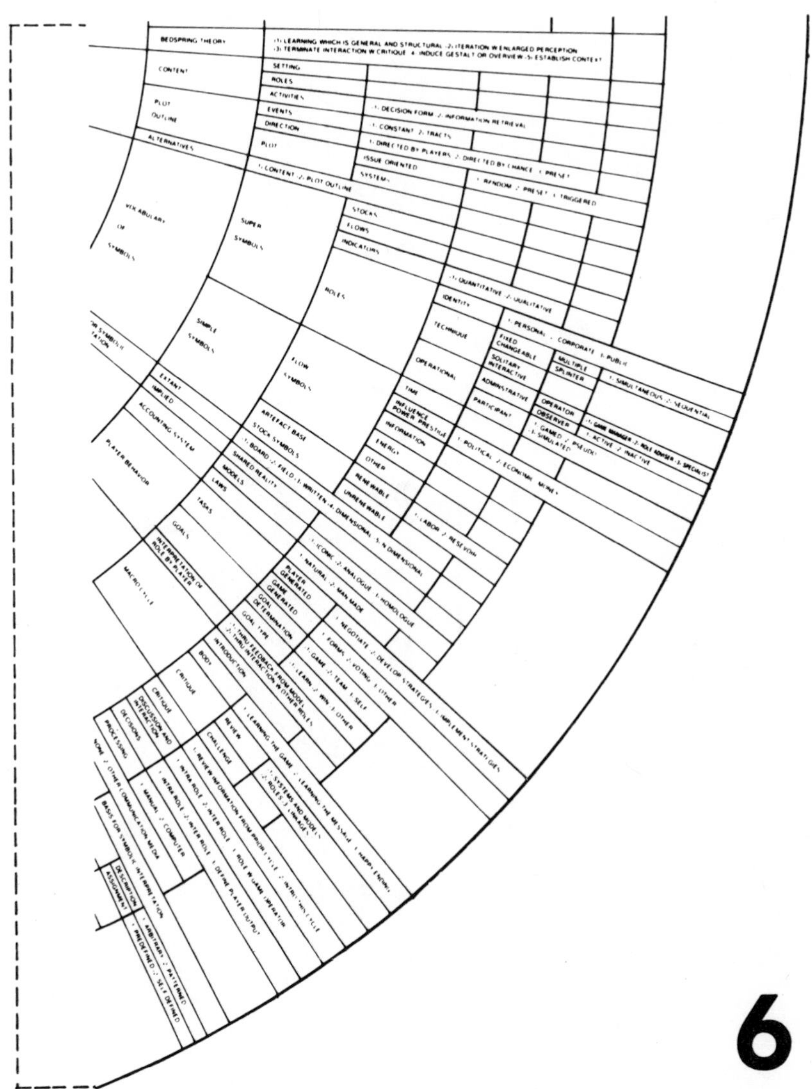

6

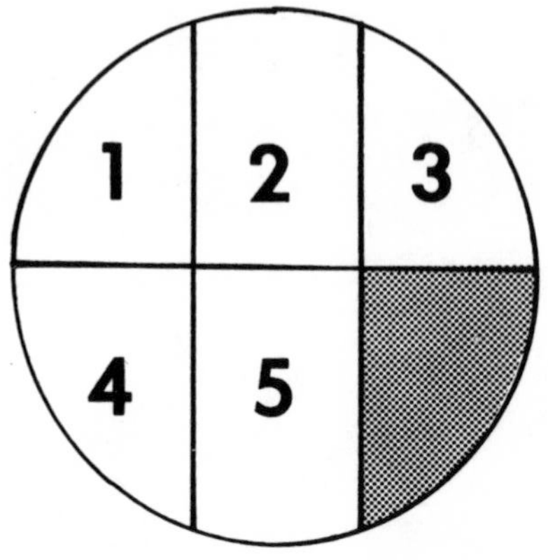
1
2
3
4
5

ABOUT THE AUTHOR

Richard de la Barre Duke is Professor of Urban and Regional Planning and Director of the Environmental Simulation Laboratory at the University of Michigan. He has developed several urban game/simulations including *Metropolis* and *METRO-APEX,* and has served as a consultant on the design and use of games in a wide variety of situations in the United States and abroad. His publications include numerous articles on gaming and a forthcoming co-authored book *Gaming/ Simulation: Rational, Design and Applications.* This book was completed while Dr. Duke was a Fellow at the Netherlands Institute for Advanced Study in the Humanities and Social Sciences in Wassenaar.